Lattice Based Interval

Brian Roberto

Contents

Chapter 1

Introduction and Preliminaries

1.1 Introduction

The theoretical structure of lattice in abstract algebra was initiated by Garrett Birkhoff [3] in 1940 and George Gratzer [11] developed the Lattice Theory in multivarious domains. L.A.Zadeh [36] discovered the most suitable mathematical kit to deal with the lack of certainty as Fuzzy Sets. The Soft Set was initiated by Molodtsov [19], [20] for dealing with the intricated problems of multivarious uncertainties and P.K.Maji [17] analysed the decision making concepts in Soft Sets. Fuzzy Soft Set was developed by P.K. Maji et al. [16]. In 2010, Pinaki [21] prolonged the generalization of Fuzzy Soft Sets. In 2009, Torra and Narukawa [24], [23] offered the Hesitant Fuzzy Set with vital properties. Correlation coefficient of Hesitant Fuzzy set was offered by Na Chen, Zeshui Xu and Meimei Xia [7]. The multi-attribute decision making based on TOPSIS method was investigated by Z.S.Xu et al [32]. In 2013, Hesitant Fuzzy Soft Set has been analysed by Babitha and John [2] and some of its basic properties was studied. Also Zheng [37], Wang [27] and Jiang-qiang [15] explored the idea of decision making over Hesitant Fuzzy Soft Sets. Further Chen [8] discovered the generalization of Hesitant Fuzzy Soft Sets. In 2009, Xibei [29] studied the Interval-Valued Fuzzy Set by combined with Soft Set and Feng Feng [9] propounded some more operations and applications of Interval-Valued Fuzzy Soft Sets in 2010. Yuncheng [35] explored the Interval-Valued Intuitionistic Fuzzy Soft Sets along with its axioms and Bivas Dinda [4] redefined operations of Interval-Valued Intuitionistic Fuzzy Soft Sets. The problem of decision making in optimistic and pessimistic views was studied by [33] Xue Wen et al.in 2014. The multivarious decision making problems has proferred by Hongwu Qin et al. [13] in 2017 and C.L.Hwang et al. [14]

In 2011, Shawkat [22] propounded the Interval-Valued Fuzzy Soft Sets with fuzzy parameters and aggregation operators technique. N.Chen et al. [6] et al examined the Interval-Valued Hesitant preference relations and their applications in 2013. In 2015, Haidong Zhang [12] initiated the concept of Interval-Valued Hesitant Fuzzy Soft Set and Xindong Peng [30] examined the technique of decision making problems on it. Also the multi-attribute decision making problems has been investigated by Yan Yang et al. [34]. Also, Manash Jyoti [18] introduced and discussed the operators on Interval-Valued Hesitant Fuzzy Soft Set.

In 2016, J.Vimala, J.Arockia Reeta [25] initiated the Lattice Ordered Fuzzy Soft Group and studied its properties [1]. The Lattice Ordered Soft Group was introduced by L.Vijayalakshmi and J.Vimala [26] in 2017. Also Distributive and Modular Lattice Ordered Fuzzy Soft Group and its duality was established in 2017.

Main Contribution:

In this present work, we introduced the concept of lattice ordered interval-valued hesitant fuzzy soft set along with its pertinent operations. The inter-related results have been proved and its properties were examined. Also we examined the operations of IVHFSS through $\mathcal{L} - \mathcal{IVHFSS}$ properties. Later the homomorphism and isomorphism on lattice ordered interval-valued hesitant fuzzy soft set was stated and the relation between $\mathcal{L}-$homomorphism and $\mathcal{L}-$isomorphism was investigated.

The notion of contra-lattice ordered interval-valued hesitant fuzzy soft set and the dual of interval-valued hesitant fuzzy soft set were discovered. Also the effect of duality in lattice ordered interval-valued hesitant fuzzy soft set and contra-lattice ordered interval-valued hesitant fuzzy soft set was examined. Also some associated theorems have been proved. Further $\mathcal{L}$-optimistic IVFSS, $\mathcal{L}$-pessimistic IVFSS and $\mathcal{L}$-neutral IVFSS have derived from $\mathcal{L} - \mathcal{IVHFSS}$. Also $\mathcal{L}$-level hesitant fuzzy soft set, contra $\mathcal{L}$-level hesitant fuzzy soft set has been inherited from a newly introduced $\mathcal{L}$-threshold IVFS and contra-$\mathcal{L}$-threshold IVFS respectively. Eventually $\mathcal{L}$-top level hesitant fuzy soft set, $\mathcal{L}$-mid level hesitant fuzzy soft set and $\mathcal{L}$-low level hesitant fuzzy soft set were defined. An efficient algorithm is constructed to solve the decision making problem through lattice ordered interval-valued hesitant fuzzy soft set. Later, the real life problem has been solved by applying this new technique via $\mathcal{L} - \mathcal{IVHFSS}$.

1.2 Preliminaries

In this section, we recall the fundamental definitions and results which are necessary for the forthcoming chapters.

Definition 1.2.1. *[36] Let X be a non-empty set, then a fuzzy set μ over X is a function from X into $I = [0, 1].ie., \mu : X \to I.$*

Definition 1.2.2. *[19] Let U and E represents universal set and set of parameters respectively. A soft set on U is defined by a pair (F, E), where F is mapping as $F : E \to P(U)$. A soft set over U is a parameterized family of subsets of the universe U.*

Definition 1.2.3. *[16] Let $F(U)$ represents the set of all fuzzy sets on U. Then a fuzzy soft set over U is a pair (F, E), where $F : E \to F(U)$ is a mapping.*

Definition 1.2.4. *[23] A hesitant fuzzy set F over U is declared interms of a function with its range is a subset of $[0, 1]$ whenever applied to U. i.e., $F = \{< x, h_F(x) > | x \in U\}$, where $h_F(x) \subseteq [0, 1]$ which gives membership degrees of the element $x \in U$ to F and is called as hesitant fuzzy element. Also H denotes the set of all hesitant fuzzy elements.*

Definition 1.2.5. *[2] Let $H(U)$ denotes the collection of all hesitant fuzzy sets on U. A* *pair* (F, E) *is called a hesitant fuzzy soft set over* U, *where* $F \colon E \to H(U)$ *is a mapping.*

Definition 1.2.6. *[31] If* $a = [a^L, a^U] = \{x | a^L \leq x \leq a^U\}$, *then* a *is said to be an interval.*

Definition 1.2.7. *[31] If* $a = [a^L, a^U]$ *and* $b = [b^L, b^U]$ *are intervals and* $\lambda > 0$, *then*

(i) $a + b = [a^L + b^L, a^U + b^U]$

(ii) $\lambda a = [\lambda a^L, \lambda a^U]$

Definition 1.2.8. *[31] Let* $a = [a^L, a^U], b = [b^L, b^U]$ *be two intervals and* $l_a = a^U - a^L$ *and* $l_b = b^U - b^L$. *Then the degree of possibility of* $a \geq b$ *is defined as* $p(a \geq b) =$ $\max\{1 - \max\{\frac{(b^U - a^L)}{(l^a + l^b)}, 0\}, 0\}$.
Similarly, $p(b \geq a) = \max\{1 - \max\{\frac{(a^U - b^L)}{(l^a + l^b)}, 0\}, 0\}$.

Definition 1.2.9. *[6] Let* $D([0,1])$ *denotes the set of all closed intervals in* $[0,1]$. *An interval-valued hesitant fuzzy set* F *over* U *is defined as* $F = \{< x, h_F(x) > | x \in U\}$, *where* $h_F \colon U \to D([0,1])$ *denotes all possible interval-valued membership degrees of the element* $x \in U$ *to the set* F. *Also* $h_F(x) = \{\nu | \nu = [\nu^L, \nu^U] \text{ is an interval}\}$ *is called as interval-valued hesitant fuzzy element (IVHFE) and is denoted as* h. *The set of all interval-valued hesitant fuzzy sets on* U *is denoted by* $IVHF(U)$.

Definition 1.2.10. *[6] The score function of an IVHFE* h *is defined as* $s\left(h\right)=\frac{\sum\limits_{\gamma\in h}\gamma}{n(h)}$,

where $n\left(h\right)$ *denotes the number of intervals in* h.

Definition 1.2.11. *[12] Let* $IVHF\left(\mathrm{U}\right)$ *denotes the collection of all interval-valued*

hesitant fuzzy sets on U. *An interval-valued hesitant fuzzy soft set is defined as a pair*

$\left(\mathrm{F},\mathrm{E}\right)$, *where* F *is such that* $\mathrm{F}\colon\mathrm{E}\to IVHF\left(\mathrm{U}\right)$ *a mapping.*

Definition 1.2.12. *[12] Let* A *and* B *be subsets of* E. *Then* $\left(\mathrm{F},\mathrm{A}\right)$ *is said to be an*

interval-valued hesitant fuzzy soft subset of $\left(\mathrm{G},\mathrm{B}\right)$ *if*

   (i) $\mathrm{A}\subseteq\mathrm{B}$

   (ii) $\gamma_{1_{\sigma(i)}}\leq\gamma_{2_{\sigma(i)}}$, *where* $\gamma_{1_{\sigma(i)}},\gamma_{2_{\sigma(i)}}$ *stands for the largest interval in the* $h_{\mathrm{F}(e_i)}\left(x\right)$

   and $h_{\mathrm{G}(e_i)}\left(x\right)$ *respectively.*

It can be written as $\left(\mathrm{F},\mathrm{A}\right)\sqsubseteq\left(\mathrm{G},\mathrm{B}\right)$

Definition 1.2.13. *[12] Let* $\left(\mathrm{F},\mathrm{A}\right)$ *and* $\left(\mathrm{G},\mathrm{B}\right)$ *be an interval-valued hesitant fuzzy soft*

sets. Then $\left(\mathrm{F},\mathrm{A}\right)$ *and* $\left(\mathrm{G},\mathrm{B}\right)$ *are interval-valued hesitant fuzzy soft equal if*

   (i) $\left(\mathrm{F},\mathrm{A}\right)\sqsubseteq\left(\mathrm{G},\mathrm{B}\right)$

   (ii) $\left(\mathrm{G},\mathrm{B}\right)\sqsubseteq\left(\mathrm{F},\mathrm{A}\right)$

It can be written as $(F, A) = (G, B)$

Definition 1.2.14. *[12] Let* (F, E) *be an interval-valued hesitant fuzzy soft set. Then its complement is defined by* (F^c, E), *where* $F^c \colon E \to IVHF(U)$ *such that* $F^c(e)$ *is the complement of interval-valued hesitant fuzzy set* $F(e)$ *on* U.

Definition 1.2.15. *[18] Let* A *and* B *be subsets of* E. *The union of two interval-valued hesitant fuzzy soft sets* (F, A) *and* (G, B) *is defined as* $(F, A) \cup (G, B) = (H, C)$, *where*

$C = A \cup B$ *and*

$$h(H(e)) = \begin{cases} h(F(e)) & \text{if } e \in A - B \\ h(G(e)) & \text{if } e \in B - A \\ h(F(e)) \cup h(G(e)) & \text{if } e \in A \cap B \end{cases}$$

Definition 1.2.16. *[18] Let* A *and* B *be subsets of* E. *The intersection of two interval-valued hesitant fuzzy soft sets* (F, A) *and* (G, B) *is defined as* $(F, A) \cap (G, B) = (H, C)$, *where* $C = A \cap B$ *and* $h(H(e)) = h(F(e)) \cap h(G(e)), \forall e \in C$.

Definition 1.2.17. *[12] Let* (F, A) *and* (G, B) *be an interval-valued hesitant fuzzy soft sets. Then* $(F, A) \wedge (G, B)$ *is defined as* $(F, A) \wedge (G, B) = (H, A \times B)$, *where*

$$H(\alpha, \beta) = \{< x, H(\alpha, \beta)(x) >: x \in U\}$$

$$= \{< x, F(\alpha)(x) \cap G(\beta)(x) >: x \in U\}$$

Definition 1.2.18. *[12] Let* (F, A) *and* (G, B) *be an interval-valued hesitant fuzzy soft* *sets. Then* $(F, A) \vee (G, B)$ *is defined as* $(F, A) \vee (G, B) = (I, A \mathrm{X} B)$ *, where*

$$I(\alpha, \beta) \;=\; \{< x, I(\alpha, \beta)(x) >: x \in U\}$$

$$\;=\; \{< x, F(\alpha)(x) \cup G(\beta)(x) >: x \in U\}$$

Definition 1.2.19. *[12] The ring sum operation on the two interval-valued hesitant fuzzy soft sets* (F, A) *and* (G, B) *over U denoted by* $F \oplus G = H$ *is a mapping given by* $H: E \to IVHF(U)$, *such that* $\forall e \in E,$

$$H(e) \;=\; \{< x, H(e)(x) >: x \in U\}$$

$$\;=\; \{< x, F(e)(x) \oplus G(e)(x) >: x \in U\}$$

Definition 1.2.20. *[12] The ring product operation on the two interval-valued hesitant fuzzy soft sets* (F, A) *and* (G, B) *over U denoted by* $F \otimes G = H$ *is a mapping given by* $H: E \to IVHF(U)$, *such that* $\forall e \in E,$

$$H(e) \;=\; \{< x, H(e)(x) >: x \in U\}$$

$$\;=\; \{< x, F(e)(x) \otimes G(e)(x) >: x \in U\}$$

Definition 1.2.21. *[12] An interval-valued hesitant fuzzy soft set is said to be an empty interval- valued hesitant fuzzy soft set if* $F : E \to IVHF(U)$ *such that*

$$
\begin{aligned}
F(e) &= \{ <x, F(e)(x)>: x \in U \} \\
&= \{ <x, [0,0]>: x \in U \}, \forall e \in E
\end{aligned}
$$

It is denoted by $\widetilde{\varnothing}$

Definition 1.2.22. *[12] An interval-valued hesitant fuzzy soft set is said to be a full interval-valued hesitant fuzzy soft set if* $F : E \to IVHF(U)$ *such that*

$$
\begin{aligned}
F(e) &= \{ <x, F(e)(x)>: x \in U \} \\
&= \{ <x, [1,1]>: x \in U \}, \forall e \in E
\end{aligned}
$$

It is denoted by $\widetilde{U}$

1.3   Summary of Thesis

This thesis is constructed as follows and it has five chapters. In Chapter I, the fundamental definitions and results which used in main results were stated.

In Chapter II, we defined and introduced the lattice ordered interval-valued hesitant fuzzy soft set with example and the related theorems were proved. Also the operations of IVHFSS have been examined.

Definition 2.1.1.

Let $(\mathcal{F}, \mathcal{P})$ be an interval-valued hesitant fuzzy soft set. Then $\mathcal{F}\left(\breve{\delta}_i\right) \subseteq \mathcal{F}\left(\breve{\delta}_j\right)$ if
$s\left(h_{\mathcal{F}}\left(\breve{\delta}_i\right)\right) \leq s\left(h_{\mathcal{F}}\left(\breve{\delta}_j\right)\right), \forall \breve{\delta}_i, \breve{\delta}_j \in \mathcal{P}$, where h is IVHFE and s is a score function.

Definition 2.1.2.

Let $(\mathcal{F}, \mathcal{P})$ be an interval-valued hesitant fuzzy soft set. We say that $(\mathcal{F}, \mathcal{P})$ a lattice
ordered interval-valued hesitant fuzzy soft set $(\mathcal{L} - \mathcal{IVHFSS})$ if $\mathcal{F}\left(\breve{\delta}_i\right) \subseteq \mathcal{F}\left(\breve{\delta}_j\right)$
whenever $\breve{\delta}_i \preceq \breve{\delta}_j, \forall \breve{\delta}_i, \breve{\delta}_j \in \mathcal{P}$.

Definition 2.1.3.

If $(\mathcal{F}, \mathcal{P})$ is $\mathcal{L} - \mathcal{IVHFSS}$ over U, then the operations $\breve{\vee}$ and $\breve{\wedge}$ are defined as

(i) $\mathcal{F}\left(\breve{\delta}_i\right) \breve{\vee} \mathcal{F}\left(\breve{\delta}_j\right) = \mathcal{F}\left(\breve{\delta}_j\right)$ and

(ii) $\mathcal{F}\left(\breve{\delta}_i\right) \breve{\wedge} \mathcal{F}\left(\breve{\delta}_j\right) = \mathcal{F}\left(\breve{\delta}_i\right)$, whenever $\breve{\delta}_i \preceq \breve{\delta}_j$

Proposition 2.1.4.

Let $(\mathcal{F}, \mathcal{P})$ be an $\mathcal{L} - \mathcal{IVHFSS}$ over U. If $\breve{\delta}_i \preceq \breve{\delta}_j$, then the following conditions are
equivalent.

(i) $\mathcal{F}\left(\breve{\delta}_i\right) \subseteq \mathcal{F}\left(\breve{\delta}_j\right)$

(ii) $\mathcal{F}\left(\breve{\delta}_i\right) \breve{\wedge} \mathcal{F}\left(\breve{\delta}_j\right) = \mathcal{F}\left(\breve{\delta}_i\right)$

(iii) $\mathcal{F}\left(\breve{\delta}_i\right) \breve{\vee} \mathcal{F}\left(\breve{\delta}_j\right) = \mathcal{F}\left(\breve{\delta}_j\right)$

Proposition 2.1.5.

(i) $[0,0]\breve{\wedge}\mathcal{F}\left(\breve{\delta}\right) = [0,0]$ and $[0,0]\breve{\vee}\mathcal{F}\left(\breve{\delta}\right) = \mathcal{F}\left(\breve{\delta}\right)$

(ii) $[0,1]\breve{\wedge}\mathcal{F}\left(\breve{\delta}\right) = \mathcal{F}\left(\breve{\delta}\right)$ and $[0,1]\breve{\vee}\mathcal{F}\left(\breve{\delta}\right) = [0,1]$.

Proposition 2.1.6.

If $(\mathcal{F}, \mathcal{P})$ is $\mathcal{L} - \mathcal{IVHFSS}$, then

(i) $\mathcal{F}\left(\breve{\delta}\right) \breve{\vee} \mathcal{F}\left(\breve{\delta}\right) = \mathcal{F}\left(\breve{\delta}\right), \mathcal{F}\left(\breve{\delta}\right) \breve{\wedge} \mathcal{F}\left(\breve{\delta}\right) = \mathcal{F}\left(\breve{\delta}\right)$

(ii) $\mathcal{F}\left(\breve{\delta}_i\right) \breve{\vee} \mathcal{F}\left(\breve{\delta}_j\right) = \mathcal{F}\left(\breve{\delta}_j\right) \breve{\vee} \mathcal{F}\left(\breve{\delta}_i\right), \mathcal{F}\left(\breve{\delta}_i\right) \breve{\wedge} \mathcal{F}\left(\breve{\delta}_j\right) = \mathcal{F}\left(\breve{\delta}_j\right) \breve{\wedge} \mathcal{F}\left(\breve{\delta}_i\right)$

(iii) $\mathcal{F}\left(\breve{\delta}_i\right) \breve{\vee} \left(\mathcal{F}\left(\breve{\delta}_j\right) \breve{\vee} \mathcal{F}\left(\breve{\delta}_k\right)\right) = \left(\mathcal{F}\left(\breve{\delta}_i\right) \breve{\vee} \mathcal{F}\left(\breve{\delta}_j\right)\right) \breve{\vee} \mathcal{F}\left(\breve{\delta}_k\right),$

$\mathcal{F}\left(\breve{\delta}_i\right) \breve{\wedge} \left(\mathcal{F}\left(\breve{\delta}_j\right) \breve{\wedge} \mathcal{F}\left(\breve{\delta}_k\right)\right) = \left(\mathcal{F}\left(\breve{\delta}_i\right) \breve{\wedge} \mathcal{F}\left(\breve{\delta}_j\right)\right) \breve{\vee} \mathcal{F}\left(\breve{\delta}_k\right)$

(iv) $\mathcal{F}\left(\breve{\delta}_i\right) \breve{\vee} \left(\mathcal{F}\left(\breve{\delta}_i\right) \breve{\wedge} \mathcal{F}\left(\breve{\delta}_j\right)\right) = \mathcal{F}\left(\breve{\delta}_i\right), \mathcal{F}\left(\breve{\delta}_i\right) \breve{\wedge} \left(\mathcal{F}\left(\breve{\delta}_i\right) \breve{\vee} \mathcal{F}\left(\breve{\delta}_j\right)\right) = \mathcal{F}\left(\breve{\delta}_i\right)$

Proposition 2.2.1.

Let $\mathbb{S} = [s^L, s^U]$ and $\mathbb{T} = [t^L, t^U]$ be two intervals with $0 \leq s^L \leq s^U \leq 1$ and

$0 \leq t^L \leq t^U \leq 1$. If $s^L < t^L$ and $s^U \geq t^U$ with $s^U - t^L > t^U - s^L$, then $P\left(\mathbb{S} \leq \mathbb{T}\right) <$

$P\left(\mathbb{S} \geq \mathbb{T}\right).$

Proposition 2.2.2.

Let $\mathbb{S} = [s^L, s^U]$ and $\mathbb{T} = [t^L, t^U]$ be two intervals with $0 \leq s^L \leq s^U \leq 1$ and $0 \leq t^L \leq t^U \leq 1$. If $s^L < t^L$ and $s^U \geq t^U$ with $t^U - s^L > s^U - t^L$, then $P\left(\mathbb{S} \geq \mathbb{T}\right) < P\left(\mathbb{S} \leq \mathbb{T}\right).$

Proposition 2.2.3

Let $\mathbb{S} = [s^L, s^U]$ and $\mathbb{T} = [t^L, t^U]$ be two intervals with $0 \leq s^L \leq s^U \leq 1$ and $0 \leq t^L \leq t^U \leq 1$. If $s^L < t^L$ and $s^U > t^U$ with $t^U - s^L = s^U - t^L$, then $P\left(\mathbb{S} \leq \mathbb{T}\right) = P\left(\mathbb{S} \geq \mathbb{T}\right).$

Proposition 2.2.4

Let $(\mathcal{F}, X)$ and $(\mathcal{G}, Y)$ be $\mathcal{L} - \mathcal{IVHFSS}$, where $X, Y \subseteq \mathcal{P}$. Then $(\mathcal{H}, Z) = (\mathcal{F}, X) \cup (\mathcal{G}, Y)$ is $\mathcal{L} - \mathcal{IVHFSS}$ if $\breve{\delta} \in X$ or $\breve{\delta} \in Y$.

Result 2.2.5

Let $X, Y \subseteq \mathcal{P}$. If $(\mathcal{F}, X)$ and $(\mathcal{G}, Y)$ are $\mathcal{L} - \mathcal{IVHFSS}$, then its union need not be $\mathcal{L} - \mathcal{IVHFSS}$ if $\breve{\delta} \in X \cap Y$.

Result 2.2.6

If $(\mathcal{F}, X)$ and $(\mathcal{G}, Y)$ are $\mathcal{L} - \mathcal{IVHFSS}$, where $X, Y \subseteq \mathcal{P}$. Then $(\mathcal{H}, Z) = (\mathcal{H}, X) \cup$

$(\mathcal{G}, Y)$ need not be $\mathcal{L} - \mathcal{IVHFSS}$ if $\breve{\delta}_i \in X$ and $\breve{\delta}_j \in Y, \forall i \neq j$.

Result 2.2.7

If $(\mathcal{F}, X)$ and $(\mathcal{G}, Y)$ are $\mathcal{L} - \mathcal{IVHFSS}$, where $X \subseteq \mathcal{P}$ and $Y \subseteq \mathcal{P}$, then its intersec-

tion need not be $\mathcal{L} - \mathcal{IVHFSS}$.

Result 2.2.8

If $(\mathcal{F}, X)$ is $\mathcal{L} - \mathcal{IVHFSS}$, then $(\mathcal{F}^c, X)$ need not be $\mathcal{L} - \mathcal{IVHFSS}$.

In Chapter III, we established the homomorphism and isomorphism between

lattice ordered interval-valued hesitant fuzzy soft sets and the main results have been

examined.

Definition 3.1.1

Let $(\mathcal{F}, \mathcal{P})$ and $(\mathcal{G}, \mathcal{P})$ be $\mathcal{L} - \mathcal{IVHFSS}$ over U. Let $S(\mathcal{F})$ and $S(\mathcal{G})$ be the set of

all score functions of $(\mathcal{F}, \mathcal{P})$ and $(\mathcal{G}, \mathcal{P})$ respectively. If a map $\varphi \colon S(\mathcal{F}) \rightarrow S(\mathcal{G})$

is 1-1, onto and $s\left(h_{\mathcal{F}}\left(\breve{\delta}_i\right)\right) \subseteq s\left(h_{\mathcal{F}}\left(\breve{\delta}_j\right)\right) \Leftrightarrow \varphi[s\left(h_{\mathcal{F}}\left(\breve{\delta}_i\right)\right)] \subseteq \varphi[s\left(h_{\mathcal{F}}\left(\breve{\delta}_j\right)\right)]$,

then φ is called as $\mathcal{L}$−isomorphism. In this case we say that $(\mathcal{F}, \mathcal{P})$ and $(\mathcal{G}, \mathcal{P})$ are

$\mathcal{L}$−isomorphic and is denoted by $(\mathcal{F}, \mathcal{P}) \approx (\mathcal{G}, \mathcal{P})$.

Definition 3.1.2.

Let $(\mathcal{F}, \mathcal{P})$ and $(\mathcal{G}, \mathcal{P})$ be $\mathcal{L} - \mathcal{IVHFSS}$ over U. Let $S(\mathcal{F})$ and $S(\mathcal{G})$ be the set of all score functions of $(\mathcal{F}, \mathcal{P})$ and $(\mathcal{G}, \mathcal{P})$ respectively. A map $\varphi \colon S(\mathcal{F}) \to S(\mathcal{G})$ is said to be a $\mathcal{L}$–homomorphism if

$$\text{(i)} \quad \varphi\left(s\left(h_{\mathcal{F}}\left(\breve{\delta}_i\right)\right) \ddot{\vee} s\left(h_{\mathcal{F}}\left(\breve{\delta}_j\right)\right)\right) = \varphi\left(s\left(h_{\mathcal{F}}\left(\breve{\delta}_i\right)\right)\right) \ddot{\vee} \varphi\left(s\left(h_{\mathcal{F}}\left(\breve{\delta}_j\right)\right)\right)$$

$$\text{(ii)} \quad \varphi\left(s\left(h_{\mathcal{F}}\left(\breve{\delta}_i\right)\right) \ddot{\wedge} s\left(h_{\mathcal{F}}\left(\breve{\delta}_j\right)\right)\right) = \varphi\left(s\left(h_{\mathcal{F}}\left(\breve{\delta}_i\right)\right)\right) \ddot{\wedge} \varphi\left(s\left(h_{\mathcal{F}}\left(\breve{\delta}_j\right)\right)\right)$$

Proposition 3.2.1.

Let $(\mathcal{F}, \mathcal{P})$ and $(\mathcal{G}, \mathcal{P})$ be $\mathcal{L} - \mathcal{IVHFSS}$ over U. Let $S(\mathcal{F})$ and $S(\mathcal{G})$ be the set of all score functions of $(\mathcal{F}, \mathcal{P})$ and $(\mathcal{G}, \mathcal{P})$ respectively. If $\varphi \colon S(\mathcal{F}) \to S(\mathcal{G})$ is a $\mathcal{L}$–homomorphism with 1-1 and onto, then φ is an $\mathcal{L}$–isomorphism.

Proposition 3.2.2.

Let $(\mathcal{F}, \mathcal{P})$ and $(\mathcal{G}, \mathcal{P})$ be $\mathcal{L} - \mathcal{IVHFSS}$ over U. Let $S(\mathcal{F})$ and $S(\mathcal{G})$ be the set of all score functions of $(\mathcal{F}, \mathcal{P})$ and $(\mathcal{G}, \mathcal{P})$ respectively. If $\varphi \colon S(\mathcal{F}) \to S(\mathcal{G})$ is onto $\mathcal{L}$–homomorphism, then the least element of $S(\mathcal{F})$ maps to the least element of $S(\mathcal{G})$.

Proposition 3.2.3.

Let $(\mathcal{F}, \mathcal{P})$ and $(\mathcal{G}, \mathcal{P})$ be $\mathcal{L} - \mathcal{IVHFSS}$ over U. Let $S(\mathcal{F})$ and $S(\mathcal{G})$ be the set of all score functions of $(\mathcal{F}, \mathcal{P})$ and $(\mathcal{G}, \mathcal{P})$ respectively. If $\varphi \colon S(\mathcal{F}) \to S(\mathcal{G})$ is onto

$\mathcal{L}-$homomorphism and $s\left(h_{\mathcal{G}}\left(\breve{\delta}_i\right)\right), s\left(h_{\mathcal{G}}\left(\breve{\delta}_j\right)\right) \in S\left(\mathcal{G}\right)$ such that $s\left(h_{\mathcal{G}}\left(\breve{\delta}_i\right)\right) \subset s\left(h_{\mathcal{G}}\left(\breve{\delta}_j\right)\right)$, then there exists $s\left(h_{\mathcal{F}}\left(\breve{\delta}_i\right)\right), s\left(h_{\mathcal{F}}\left(\breve{\delta}_j\right)\right) \in S\left(\mathcal{F}\right)$ such that $\varphi\left(s\left(h_{\mathcal{F}}\left(\breve{\delta}_i\right)\right)\right) = s\left(h_{\mathcal{G}}\left(\breve{\delta}_i\right)\right), \varphi\left(s\left(h_{\mathcal{F}}\left(\breve{\delta}_j\right)\right)\right) = s\left(h_{\mathcal{G}}\left(\breve{\delta}_j\right)\right)$ and $s\left(h_{\mathcal{F}}\left(\breve{\delta}_i\right)\right) \subset s\left(h_{\mathcal{F}}\left(\breve{\delta}_j\right)\right)$

In chapter IV, we introduced the contra-lattice ordered interval-valued hesitant fuzzy soft set and described the duality in lattice ordered interval-valued hesitant fuzzy soft set. Also the impact of duality in contra-lattice ordered interval-valued hesitant fuzzy soft set was analysed.

Definition 4.1.1.

Let $\mathcal{P}$ and $\mathcal{Q}$ be parameter sets. Let $(\mathcal{F}, \mathcal{P})$ be an IVHFSS over U . A dual of $(\mathcal{F}, \mathcal{P})$ is defined as an IVHFSS $(\mathcal{F}, \mathcal{Q})$ if $\mathcal{F}\left(\breve{\delta}_i\right) \subseteq \mathcal{F}\left(\breve{\delta}_j\right) \Leftrightarrow \mathcal{F}\left(\breve{\varepsilon}_i\right) \supseteq \mathcal{F}\left(\breve{\varepsilon}_j\right), \forall \varrho \in$ U.

Definition 4.1.2.

Let $(\mathcal{F}, \mathcal{P})$ be an IVHFSS over U. If $\mathcal{F}\left(\breve{\varepsilon}_i\right) \supseteq \mathcal{F}\left(\breve{\varepsilon}_j\right)$, whenever $\breve{\varepsilon}_i \preceq \breve{\varepsilon}_j, \forall \breve{\varepsilon}_i, \breve{\varepsilon}_j \in \mathcal{P}$, then $(\mathcal{F}, \mathcal{P})$ is called as a contra-lattice ordered interval-valued hesitant fuzzy soft set. It can be simply written as $Contra - \mathcal{L} - \mathcal{IVHFSS}$.

Proposition 4.2.1.

Let $(\mathcal{F}, \mathcal{P})$ be a lattice ordered interval-valued hesitant fuzzy soft set over U. Then its dual is $Contra - \mathcal{L} - \mathcal{IVHFSS}$.

Proposition 4.2.2.

If $(\mathcal{G}, \mathcal{P})$ is $Contra - \mathcal{L} - \mathcal{IVHFSS}$ over U, then its dual is $\mathcal{L} - \mathcal{IVHFSS}$.

Proposition 4.2.3.

If $(\mathcal{F}, \mathcal{P})$ is an $\mathcal{L} - \mathcal{IVHFSS}$, then there exists an $\mathcal{L}-$isomorphism between $(\mathcal{F}, \mathcal{P})$ and the dual of its dual.

In Chapter V, the new conceptions has been inherited from interval-valued fuzzy soft sets and an efficient algorithm for handling a decision making problem was constructed.

Definition 5.2.1.

Let $(\mathcal{F}, \mathcal{P})$ be an $\mathcal{L} - \mathcal{IVHFSS}$ over U. Then $\mathcal{L}$-optimistic interval-valued fuzzy soft set $(\mathcal{F}_{\mathcal{L}+}, \mathcal{P})$ is defined as

$$
\begin{aligned}
(\mathcal{F}_{\mathcal{L}+}, \mathcal{P}) &= \{< x, \mathcal{F}_{\mathcal{L}+}\left(\breve{\delta}\right)(x) > | x \in U\} \\
&= \{< x, \vee\gamma_{\mathcal{L}}^{\sigma(k)} > | x \in U\},
\end{aligned}
$$

$\forall \breve{\delta} \in \mathcal{P}$ and $\forall k = 1, 2..n,$

where $\gamma_{\mathcal{L}}^{\sigma(k)} = [\gamma_{\mathcal{L}}^{\sigma(k)(L)}, \gamma_{\mathcal{L}}^{\sigma(k)(U)}] \in \mathcal{F}\left(\breve{\delta}\right)(x)$

Definition 5.2.2.

Let $(\mathcal{F}, \mathcal{P})$ be an $\mathcal{L} - \mathcal{IVHFSS}$ over U. Then $\mathcal{L}$-neutral interval-valued fuzzy soft set

$(\mathcal{F}_{\mathcal{L}\sim}, \mathcal{P})$ is defined as

$$
\begin{aligned}
(\mathcal{F}_{\mathcal{L}\sim}, \mathcal{P}) &= \{< x, \mathcal{F}_{\mathcal{L}\sim}\left(\breve{\delta}\right)(x) > |x \in U\} \\
&= \{< x, \sum_{k=1}^{n} \frac{\gamma_{\mathcal{L}}^{\sigma(k)}}{n} > |x \in U\},
\end{aligned}
$$

$\forall \breve{\delta} \in \mathcal{P}$ and $\forall k = 1, 2..n$, where $\gamma_{\mathcal{L}}^{\sigma(k)} = [\gamma_{\mathcal{L}}^{\sigma(k)(L)}, \gamma_{\mathcal{L}}^{\sigma(k)(U)}] \in \mathcal{F}\left(\breve{\delta}\right)(x)$

Definition 5.2.3.

Let $(\mathcal{F}, \mathcal{P})$ be an $\mathcal{L} - \mathcal{IVHFSS}$ over U. Then $\mathcal{L}$-pessimistic interval-valued fuzzy

soft set $(\mathcal{F}_{\mathcal{L}-}, \mathcal{P})$ is defined as

$$
\begin{aligned}
(\mathcal{F}_{\mathcal{L}-}, \mathcal{P}) &= \{< x, \mathcal{F}_{\mathcal{L}-}\left(\breve{\delta}\right)(x) > |x \in U\} \\
&= \{< x, \wedge \gamma_{\mathcal{L}}^{\sigma(k)} > |x \in U\},
\end{aligned}
$$

$\forall \breve{\delta} \in \mathcal{P}$ and $\forall k = 1, 2..n$, where $\gamma_{\mathcal{L}}^{\sigma(k)} = [\gamma_{\mathcal{L}}^{\sigma(k)(L)}, \gamma_{\mathcal{L}}^{\sigma(k)(U)}] \in \mathcal{F}\left(\breve{\delta}\right)(x)$

Definition 5.2.4.

Let $(\mathcal{F}, \mathcal{P})$ be an $\mathcal{L} - \mathcal{IVHFSS}$ over U and $(I, \mathcal{P})$ be an IVFS. Then

$$\alpha^{\sigma(k)} = \begin{cases} 1 & \text{if } \gamma^{\sigma(k)} \geq I\left(\breve{\delta}\right) \\ 0 & \text{if } \gamma^{\sigma(k)} < I\left(\breve{\delta}\right) \end{cases}, \forall \breve{\delta} \in \mathcal{P}, \forall \gamma^{\sigma(k)} \in \mathcal{F}\left(\breve{\delta}\right) \text{ and } \forall k = 1, 2..n. \text{ Then}$$

$(I, \mathcal{P})$ is called an $\mathcal{L}$-threshold interval-valued fuzzy set. Also an $\mathcal{L}$-level hesitant fuzzy

soft set $(\mathcal{F}_{\mathcal{L}I}, \mathcal{P})$ with respect to $(I, \mathcal{P})$ is defined as

$$\begin{aligned} (\mathcal{F}_{\mathcal{L}I}, \mathcal{P}) &= \{< x, \mathcal{F}_{\mathcal{L}I}\left(\breve{\delta}\right)(x) > | x \in U\} \\ &= \{< x, \{\alpha^{\sigma(k)}\} > | x \in U\}, \end{aligned}$$

$\forall \breve{\delta} \in \mathcal{P}, \forall k = 1, 2...n$

Definition 5.2.5.

Let $(\mathcal{F}, \mathcal{P})$ be an $\mathcal{L} - \mathcal{IVHFSS}$ over U and $(J, \mathcal{P})$ be an IVFS. Then

$$\beta^{\sigma(k)} = \begin{cases} 1 & \text{if } \gamma^{\sigma(k)} \leq J\left(\breve{\delta}\right) \\ 0 & \text{if } \gamma^{\sigma(k)} > J\left(\breve{\delta}\right) \end{cases}, \forall \breve{\delta} \in \mathcal{P}, \forall \gamma^{\sigma(k)} \in \mathcal{F}\left(\breve{\delta}\right) \text{ and } \forall k = 1, 2..n. \text{ Then}$$

$(J, \mathcal{P})$ is called a contra-$\mathcal{L}$-threshold interval-valued fuzzy set. Also a contra-$\mathcal{L}$-level

hesitant fuzzy soft set $(\mathcal{F}_{\mathcal{L}J}, \mathcal{P})$ with respect to $(J, \mathcal{P})$ is defined as

$$\begin{aligned} (\mathcal{F}_{\mathcal{L}J}, \mathcal{P}) &= \{< x, \mathcal{F}_{\mathcal{L}J}\left(\breve{\delta}\right)(x) > | x \in U\} \\ &= \{< x, \{\beta^{\sigma(k)}\} > | x \in U\}, \end{aligned}$$

$\forall \breve{\delta} \in \mathcal{P}, \forall k = 1, 2...n$

Definition 5.2.6.

Let U be an universal set and $\mathcal{P}$ be a parameter set. Let $(\mathcal{F}, \mathcal{P})$ be $\mathcal{L} - \mathcal{IVHFSS}$.

Then

(i) $\ddot{\vee}_{x \in U}\{\mathcal{F}\left(\breve{\delta}\right)(x)\} = \mathcal{F}\left(\breve{\delta}\right)(x_k)$ if $\mathcal{F}\left(\breve{\delta}\right)(x_i) \subseteq \mathcal{F}\left(\breve{\delta}\right)(x_j) \subseteq \mathcal{F}\left(\breve{\delta}\right)(x_k)$

(ii) $\ddot{\wedge}_{x \in U}\{\mathcal{F}\left(\breve{\delta}\right)(x)\} = \mathcal{F}\left(\breve{\delta}\right)(x_i)$ if $\mathcal{F}\left(\breve{\delta}\right)(x_i) \subseteq \mathcal{F}\left(\breve{\delta}\right)(x_j) \subseteq \mathcal{F}\left(\breve{\delta}\right)(x_k)$

(iii) $\ddot{\vee}\ddot{\wedge}_{x \in U}\{\mathcal{F}\left(\breve{\delta}\right)(x)\} = \mathcal{F}\left(\breve{\delta}\right)(x_j)$ if $\mathcal{F}\left(\breve{\delta}\right)(x_i) \subseteq \mathcal{F}\left(\breve{\delta}\right)(x_j) \subseteq \mathcal{F}\left(\breve{\delta}\right)(x_k)$.

Definition 5.2.7.

Let $(\mathcal{F}, \mathcal{P})$ be an $\mathcal{L} - \mathcal{IVHFSS}$ over U and $(\mathcal{F}_{\mathcal{L}+}, \mathcal{P})$ be an $\mathcal{L}$-optimistic IVFSS over

U. Then $Max_{\mathcal{L}}$-threshold of $\mathcal{L} - \mathcal{IVHFSS}$ is defined as $\mathcal{F}_{Max-\mathcal{L}}\left(\breve{\delta}\right) = \ddot{\vee}\mathcal{F}_{\mathcal{L}+}\left(\breve{\delta}\right)(x)$,

$\forall \breve{\delta} \in \mathcal{P}$, where $x \in U$. The $\mathcal{L}$-top level Hfss of $(\mathcal{F}, \mathcal{P})$ with respect to $Max_{\mathcal{L}}$-threshold

is defined as $(\mathcal{F}_{Max-\mathcal{L}}, \mathcal{P}) = \{< x, \mathcal{F}_{Max-\mathcal{L}}\left(\breve{\delta}\right)(x) > | x \in U\}$.

Definition 5.2.8.

Let $(\mathcal{F}, \mathcal{P})$ be an $\mathcal{L} - \mathcal{IVHFSS}$ over U and $(\mathcal{F}_{\mathcal{L}\sim}, \mathcal{P})$ be an $\mathcal{L}$-neutral IVFSS over U.

Then $Mid_{\mathcal{L}}$-threshold of $\mathcal{L} - \mathcal{IVHFSS}$ is defined as $\mathcal{F}_{Mid-\mathcal{L}}\left(\breve{\delta}\right) = \ddot{\vee}\ddot{\wedge}\mathcal{F}_{\mathcal{L}\sim}\left(\breve{\delta}\right)(x)$,

$\forall \breve{\delta} \in \mathcal{P}$, where $x \in U$. The $\mathcal{L}$-mid level Hfss of $(\mathcal{F}, \mathcal{P})$ with respect to $Mid_{\mathcal{L}}$-threshold

is defined as $(\mathcal{F}_{Mid-\mathcal{L}}, \mathcal{P}) = \{< x, \mathcal{F}_{Mid-\mathcal{L}}\left(\breve{\delta}\right)(x) > | x \in U\}$.

Definition 5.2.9.

Let $(\mathcal{F}, \mathcal{P})$ be an $\mathcal{L} - \mathcal{IVHFSS}$ over U and $(\mathcal{F}_{\mathcal{L}-}, \mathcal{P})$ be an $\mathcal{L}$-pessimistic IVFSS over U. Then $Min_{\mathcal{L}}$-threshold of $\mathcal{L} - \mathcal{IVHFSS}$ is defined as $\mathcal{F}_{Min-\mathcal{L}}\left(\breve{\delta}\right) = \ddot{\wedge}\mathcal{F}_{\mathcal{L}-}\left(\breve{\delta}\right)(x)$, $\forall \breve{\delta} \in \mathcal{P}$, where $x \in U$. The $\mathcal{L}$-low level Hfss of $(\mathcal{F}, \mathcal{P})$ with respect to $Min_{\mathcal{L}}$-threshold is defined as $(\mathcal{F}_{Min-\mathcal{L}}, \mathcal{P}) = \{< x, \mathcal{F}_{Min-\mathcal{L}}\left(\breve{\delta}\right)(x) > |x \in U\}$.

Later the real life problem was solved by using this algorithm via lattice ordered interval-valued hesitant fuzzy soft set.

Chapter 2

Lattice Ordered Interval-Valued Hesitant Fuzzy Soft Sets

---

[1]   This chapter has two sections. In the first section, we introduced the lattice

ordered interval-valued hesitant fuzzy soft set with examples. Also the important theo-

rems and results were proved. In the next section, we examined the lattice approaches

in the operations of interval-valued hesitant fuzzy soft set produce whether L-IVHFSS

or not.

2.1   Lattice Ordered Interval-Valued Hesitant Fuzzy Soft Set

Definition 2.1.1. *Let $(\mathcal{F}, \mathcal{P})$ be an interval-valued hesitant fuzzy soft set. Then $\mathcal{F}\left(\breve{\delta}_i\right) \subseteq$*

$\mathcal{F}\left(\breve{\delta}_j\right)$ *if* $s\left(h_{\mathcal{F}}\left(\breve{\delta}_i\right)\right) \leq s\left(h_{\mathcal{F}}\left(\breve{\delta}_j\right)\right)$, $\forall \breve{\delta}_i, \breve{\delta}_j \in \mathcal{P}$, *where h is IVHFE and s is a score*

---
[1]International Journal of Engineering & Technology

function.

Definition 2.1.2. *Let* $(\mathcal{F}, \mathcal{P})$ *be an interval-valued hesitant fuzzy soft set. We say that* $(\mathcal{F}, \mathcal{P})$ *a lattice ordered interval-valued hesitant fuzzy soft set* $(\mathcal{L} - \mathcal{IVHFSS})$ *if* $\mathcal{F}\left(\breve{\delta}_i\right) \subseteq \mathcal{F}\left(\breve{\delta}_j\right)$ *whenever* $\breve{\delta}_i \preceq \breve{\delta}_j, \forall \breve{\delta}_i, \breve{\delta}_j \in \mathcal{P}.$

Example 1.

Let $U = \{x_1, x_2\}$ represents bike, car respectively and $\mathcal{P} = \{\breve{\delta}_1, \breve{\delta}_2, \breve{\delta}_3\}$ represents

the years 2015, 2016 and 2017 respectively. Then $(\mathcal{F}, \mathcal{P})$ is a $\mathcal{L} - \mathcal{IVHFSS}$ which

represents the sales of bike and car of two particular showrooms in the relevant years as

follows,

$$(\mathcal{F}, \mathcal{P}) = \{\mathcal{F}\left(\breve{\delta}_1\right) = \{< x_1, \{[0.1, 0.3], [0.2, 0.4]\} >, < x_2, \{[0.2, 0.4], [0.2, 0.3]\} >\},$$

$$\mathcal{F}\left(\breve{\delta}_2\right) = \{< x_1, \{[0.3, 0.4], [0.3, 0.5]\} >, < x_2, \{[0.1, 0.4], [0.4, 0.7]\} >\},$$

$$\mathcal{F}\left(\breve{\delta}_3\right) = \{< x_1, \{[0.4, 0.5], [0.45, 0.6]\} >, < x_2, \{[0.4, 0.6], [0.4, 0.6]\} >\}\}.$$

Definition 2.1.3. *If* $(\mathcal{F}, \mathcal{P})$ *is* $\mathcal{L} - \mathcal{IVHFSS}$ *over* U, *then the operations* $\breve{\vee}$ *and* $\breve{\wedge}$ *are defined as*

(i) $\mathcal{F}\left(\breve{\delta}_i\right) \breve{\vee} \mathcal{F}\left(\breve{\delta}_j\right) = \mathcal{F}\left(\breve{\delta}_j\right)$ *and*

(ii) $\mathcal{F}\left(\breve{\delta}_i\right)\bar{\wedge}\mathcal{F}\left(\breve{\delta}_j\right)=\mathcal{F}\left(\breve{\delta}_i\right)$, whenever $\breve{\delta}_i\preceq\breve{\delta}_j$

Proposition 2.1.4. *Let* $(\mathcal{F},\mathcal{P})$ *be an* $\mathcal{L}-\mathcal{IVHFSS}$ *over* U. *If* $\breve{\delta}_i\preceq\breve{\delta}_j$, *then the*

following conditions are equivalent.

(i) $\mathcal{F}\left(\breve{\delta}_i\right)\subseteq\mathcal{F}\left(\breve{\delta}_j\right)$

(ii) $\mathcal{F}\left(\breve{\delta}_i\right)\bar{\wedge}\mathcal{F}\left(\breve{\delta}_j\right)=\mathcal{F}\left(\breve{\delta}_i\right)$

(iii) $\mathcal{F}\left(\breve{\delta}_i\right)\bar{\vee}\mathcal{F}\left(\breve{\delta}_j\right)=\mathcal{F}\left(\breve{\delta}_j\right)$

Proposition 2.1.5. (i) $[0,0]\bar{\wedge}\mathcal{F}\left(\breve{\delta}\right)=[0,0]$ *and* $[0,0]\bar{\vee}\mathcal{F}\left(\breve{\delta}\right)=\mathcal{F}\left(\breve{\delta}\right)$

(ii) $[0,1]\bar{\wedge}\mathcal{F}\left(\breve{\delta}\right)=\mathcal{F}\left(\breve{\delta}\right)$ *and* $[0,1]\bar{\vee}\mathcal{F}\left(\breve{\delta}\right)=[0,1]$.

Proposition 2.1.6. *If* $(\mathcal{F},\mathcal{P})$ *is* $\mathcal{L}-\mathcal{IVHFSS}$, *then*

(i) $\mathcal{F}\left(\breve{\delta}\right)\bar{\vee}\mathcal{F}\left(\breve{\delta}\right)=\mathcal{F}\left(\breve{\delta}\right),\mathcal{F}\left(\breve{\delta}\right)\bar{\wedge}\mathcal{F}\left(\breve{\delta}\right)=\mathcal{F}\left(\breve{\delta}\right)$

(ii) $\mathcal{F}\left(\breve{\delta}_i\right)\bar{\vee}\mathcal{F}\left(\breve{\delta}_j\right)=\mathcal{F}\left(\breve{\delta}_j\right)\bar{\vee}\mathcal{F}\left(\breve{\delta}_i\right),\mathcal{F}\left(\breve{\delta}_i\right)\bar{\wedge}\mathcal{F}\left(\breve{\delta}_j\right)=\mathcal{F}\left(\breve{\delta}_j\right)\bar{\wedge}\mathcal{F}\left(\breve{\delta}_i\right)$

(iii) $\mathcal{F}\left(\breve{\delta}_i\right)\bar{\vee}\left(\mathcal{F}\left(\breve{\delta}_j\right)\bar{\vee}\mathcal{F}\left(\breve{\delta}_k\right)\right)=\left(\mathcal{F}\left(\breve{\delta}_i\right)\bar{\vee}\mathcal{F}\left(\breve{\delta}_j\right)\right)\bar{\vee}\mathcal{F}\left(\breve{\delta}_k\right)$,

$\qquad\mathcal{F}\left(\breve{\delta}_i\right)\bar{\wedge}\left(\mathcal{F}\left(\breve{\delta}_j\right)\bar{\wedge}\mathcal{F}\left(\breve{\delta}_k\right)\right)=\left(\mathcal{F}\left(\breve{\delta}_i\right)\bar{\wedge}\mathcal{F}\left(\breve{\delta}_j\right)\right)\bar{\vee}\mathcal{F}\left(\breve{\delta}_k\right)$

(iv) $\mathcal{F}\left(\breve{\delta}_i\right) \mathbin{\breve{\vee}} \left(\mathcal{F}\left(\breve{\delta}_i\right) \mathbin{\breve{\wedge}} \mathcal{F}\left(\breve{\delta}_j\right)\right) = \mathcal{F}\left(\breve{\delta}_i\right), \mathcal{F}\left(\breve{\delta}_i\right) \mathbin{\breve{\wedge}} \left(\mathcal{F}\left(\breve{\delta}_i\right) \mathbin{\breve{\vee}} \mathcal{F}\left(\breve{\delta}_j\right)\right) = \mathcal{F}\left(\breve{\delta}_i\right)$

Proof. (i) *Idempotency:*

Clearly $\mathcal{F}\left(\breve{\delta}\right) \mathbin{\breve{\vee}} \mathcal{F}\left(\breve{\delta}\right) = \mathcal{F}\left(\breve{\delta}\right)$ and $\mathcal{F}\left(\breve{\delta}\right) \mathbin{\breve{\wedge}} \mathcal{F}\left(\breve{\delta}\right) = \mathcal{F}\left(\breve{\delta}\right)$.

(ii)*Commutativity:*

$\mathcal{F}\left(\breve{\delta}_i\right) \mathbin{\breve{\vee}} \mathcal{F}\left(\breve{\delta}_j\right) = \max\{\mathcal{F}\left(\breve{\delta}_i\right), \mathcal{F}\left(\breve{\delta}_j\right)\} = \max\{\mathcal{F}\left(\breve{\delta}_j\right), \mathcal{F}\left(\breve{\delta}_i\right)\} = \mathcal{F}\left(\breve{\delta}_j\right) \mathbin{\breve{\vee}} \mathcal{F}\left(\breve{\delta}_i\right)$

$\mathcal{F}\left(\breve{\delta}_i\right) \mathbin{\breve{\wedge}} \mathcal{F}\left(\breve{\delta}_j\right) = \min\{\mathcal{F}\left(\breve{\delta}_i\right), \mathcal{F}\left(\breve{\delta}_j\right)\} = \min\{\mathcal{F}\left(\breve{\delta}_j\right), \mathcal{F}\left(\breve{\delta}_i\right)\} = \mathcal{F}\left(\breve{\delta}_j\right) \mathbin{\breve{\wedge}} \mathcal{F}\left(\breve{\delta}_i\right)$.

(iii)*Associativity:*

Since $\mathcal{F}\left(\breve{\delta}_i\right) \subseteq \mathcal{F}\left(\breve{\delta}_j\right) \subseteq \mathcal{F}\left(\breve{\delta}_k\right)$.

$\Rightarrow \mathcal{F}\left(\breve{\delta}_j\right) \mathbin{\breve{\vee}} \mathcal{F}\left(\breve{\delta}_k\right) = \mathcal{F}\left(\breve{\delta}_k\right)$ and $\mathcal{F}\left(\breve{\delta}_i\right) \mathbin{\breve{\vee}} \mathcal{F}\left(\breve{\delta}_k\right) = \mathcal{F}\left(\breve{\delta}_k\right)$

$\Rightarrow \mathcal{F}\left(\breve{\delta}_i\right) \mathbin{\breve{\vee}} \left(\mathcal{F}\left(\breve{\delta}_j\right) \vee \mathcal{F}\left(\breve{\delta}_k\right)\right) = \mathcal{F}\left(\breve{\delta}_k\right)$

Now, $\mathcal{F}\left(\breve{\delta}_i\right) \mathbin{\breve{\vee}} \mathcal{F}\left(\breve{\delta}_j\right) = \mathcal{F}\left(\breve{\delta}_j\right)$

$\Rightarrow \left(\mathcal{F}\left(\breve{\delta}_i\right) \mathbin{\breve{\vee}} \mathcal{F}\left(\breve{\delta}_j\right)\right) \mathbin{\breve{\vee}} \mathcal{F}\left(\breve{\delta}_k\right) = \mathcal{F}\left(\breve{\delta}_j\right) \mathbin{\breve{\vee}} \mathcal{F}\left(\breve{\delta}_k\right) = \mathcal{F}\left(\breve{\delta}_k\right)$.

Hence we have $\mathcal{F}\left(\breve{\delta}_i\right) \vee \left(\mathcal{F}\left(\breve{\delta}_j\right) \mathbin{\breve{\vee}} \mathcal{F}\left(\breve{\delta}_k\right)\right) = \left(\mathcal{F}\left(\breve{\delta}_i\right) \mathbin{\breve{\vee}} \mathcal{F}\left(\breve{\delta}_j\right)\right) \mathbin{\breve{\vee}} \mathcal{F}\left(\breve{\delta}_k\right)$ and

Similarly $\mathcal{F}\left(\breve{\delta}_i\right) \mathbin{\breve{\wedge}} \left(\mathcal{F}\left(\breve{\delta}_j\right) \mathbin{\breve{\wedge}} \mathcal{F}\left(\breve{\delta}_k\right)\right) = \left(\mathcal{F}\left(\breve{\delta}_i\right) \mathbin{\breve{\wedge}} \mathcal{F}\left(\breve{\delta}_j\right)\right) \mathbin{\breve{\vee}} \mathcal{F}\left(\breve{\delta}_k\right)$

(iv)*Absorption:*

Suppose $\mathcal{F}\left(\breve{\delta}_i\right) \mathbin{\breve{\wedge}} \mathcal{F}\left(\breve{\delta}_j\right) = \mathcal{F}\left(\breve{\delta}_i\right)$

Then $\mathcal{F}\left(\breve{\delta}_i\right) \breve{\vee} \left(\mathcal{F}\left(\breve{\delta}_i\right) \breve{\wedge} \mathcal{F}\left(\breve{\delta}_j\right)\right) = \mathcal{F}\left(\breve{\delta}_i\right) \breve{\vee} \mathcal{F}\left(\breve{\delta}_i\right) = \mathcal{F}\left(\breve{\delta}_i\right)$.

Also $\mathcal{F}\left(\breve{\delta}_i\right) \breve{\vee} \mathcal{F}\left(\breve{\delta}_j\right) = \mathcal{F}\left(\breve{\delta}_j\right)$

$\Rightarrow \mathcal{F}\left(\breve{\delta}_i\right) \breve{\wedge} \left(\mathcal{F}\left(\breve{\delta}_i\right) \breve{\vee} \mathcal{F}\left(\breve{\delta}_j\right)\right) = \mathcal{F}\left(\breve{\delta}_i\right) \breve{\wedge} \mathcal{F}\left(\breve{\delta}_j\right) = \mathcal{F}\left(\breve{\delta}_i\right)$. $\qquad\square$

2.2 Properties of Operations in L-IVHFSS

Proposition 2.2.1. *Let* $\mathbb{S} = [s^L, s^U]$ *and* $\mathbb{T} = [t^L, t^U]$ *be two intervals with*

$0 \leq s^L \leq s^U \leq 1$ *and* $0 \leq t^L \leq t^U \leq 1$. *If* $s^L < t^L$ *and* $s^U \geq t^U$ *with*

$s^U - t^L > t^U - s^L$, *then* $P\left(\mathbb{S} \leq \mathbb{T}\right) < P\left(\mathbb{S} \geq \mathbb{T}\right)$.

Proof. Suppose $s^L < t^L$ and $s^U \geq t^U$ with $s^U - t^L > s^U - t^L$

Then $s^U - t^L \geq t^U - t^L > t^U - s^L \Rightarrow s^U - t^L > t^U - s^L \Rightarrow \frac{s^U - t^L}{l_s + l_t} > \frac{t^U - s^L}{l_s + l_t}$

Since $t^L < t^U \geq s^U \Rightarrow s^U - t^L > 0 \Rightarrow \frac{s^U - t^L}{l_s + l_t} > 0$

$\Rightarrow Max\left\{\frac{s^U - t^L}{l_s + l_t}, o\right\} = \frac{s^U - t^L}{l_s + l_t}$

$\Rightarrow 1 - Max\left\{\frac{s^U - t^L}{l_s + l_t}, o\right\} = 1 - \frac{s^U - t^L}{l_s + l_t} = \frac{t^U - s^L}{l_s + l_t}$

Since $s^L < s^U, t^L < t^U, s^L < t^L$ and $s^U \geq t^U$

$\Rightarrow s^L < t^L < t^U \geq s^U \Rightarrow t^U - s^L > 0 \Rightarrow \frac{t^U - s^L}{l_s + l_t} > 0$

$P(s \leq t) = \frac{t^U - s^L}{l_s + l_t}$

Since $s^L < t^L < t^U \Rightarrow t^U - s^L > 0 \Rightarrow \frac{t^U - s^L}{l_s + l_t} > 0$

$Max\left\{\frac{t^U - s^L}{l_s + l_t}, 0\right\} = \frac{t^U - s^L}{l_s + l_t} \Rightarrow 1 - Max\left\{\frac{s^U - t^L}{l_s + l_t}, o\right\} = 1 - \frac{s^U - t^L}{l_s + l_t} = \frac{s^U - t^L}{l_s + l_t} > 0$

$P(\mathbb{S} \geq \mathbb{T}) = \frac{s^U - t^L}{l_s + l_t} \Rightarrow P(\mathbb{S} \leq \mathbb{T}) = \frac{t^U - s^L}{l_s + l_t} < \frac{s^U - t^L}{l_s + l_t} = P(\mathbb{S} \geq \mathbb{T})$

$\Rightarrow P(\mathbb{S} \leq \mathbb{T}) < P(\mathbb{S} \geq \mathbb{T})$ $\qquad\qquad\qquad\qquad\qquad\qquad\qquad$ $\square$

Proposition 2.2.2. *Let* $\mathbb{S} = [s^L, s^U]$ *and* $\mathbb{T} = [t^L, t^U]$ *be two intervals with* $0 \leq s^L \leq s^U \leq 1$ *and* $0 \leq t^L \leq t^U \leq 1$. *If* $s^L < t^L$ *and* $s^U \geq t^U$ *with* $t^U - s^L > s^U - t^L$, *then* $P(\mathbb{S} \geq \mathbb{T}) < P(\mathbb{S} \leq \mathbb{T})$.

Proof. Suppose $s^L < t^L$ and $s^U \geq t^U$ with $t^U - s^L > s^U - t^L$

Since $s^L < s^U, t^L < t^U \Rightarrow s^L < t^L < t^U \leq s^U \Rightarrow \frac{t^U - s^L}{l_s + l_t} > 0$

$Max\left\{\frac{t^U - s^L}{l_s + l_t}, o\right\} = \frac{t^U - s^L}{l_s + l_t} \Rightarrow 1 - Max\left\{\frac{t^U - s^L}{l_s + l_t}, o\right\} = 1 - \frac{t^U - s^L}{l_s + l_t} = \frac{s^U - t^L}{l_s + l_t}$

Since $t^L < t^U \leq s^U \Rightarrow s^U - t^L > 0 \Rightarrow \frac{s^U - t^L}{l_s + l_t} > 0$

$Max\left\{\frac{s^U - t^L}{l_s + l_t}, o\right\} = \frac{s^U - t^L}{l_s + l_t} \Rightarrow 1 - Max\left\{\frac{s^U - t^L}{l_s + l_t}, o\right\} = 1 - \frac{s^U - t^L}{l_s + l_t} = \frac{t^U - s^L}{l_s + l_t} > 0$

$P(\mathbb{S} \leq \mathbb{T}) = \frac{t^U - s^L}{l_s + l_t}$

$P(\mathbb{S} \geq \mathbb{T}) = \frac{s^U - t^L}{l_s + l_t} < \frac{s^U - s^L}{l_s + l_t} = P(\mathbb{S} \leq \mathbb{T})$ $\qquad\qquad\qquad\qquad$ $\square$

Proposition 2.2.3. *Let* $\mathbb{S} = [s^L, s^U]$ *and* $\mathbb{T} = [t^L, t^U]$ *be two intervals with* $0 \leq s^L \leq s^U \leq 1$ *and* $0 \leq t^L \leq t^U \leq 1$. *If* $s^L < t^L$ *and* $s^U > t^U$ *with* $t^U - s^L = s^U - t^L$, *then* $P\left(\mathbb{S} \le \mathbb{T}\right) = P\left(\mathbb{S} \ge \mathbb{T}\right)$.

Proof. Suppose $s^L < t^L$ and $s^U > t^U$ with $t^U - s^L = s^U - t^L$

$$s^L < s^U, s^L < t^L, t^L < t^U, t^U < s^U \Rightarrow s^L < t^L < t^U < s^U \Rightarrow t^U - s^L > 0$$

$$\Rightarrow \frac{t^U - s^L}{l_s + l_t} > 0 \Rightarrow Max\left\{\frac{t^U - s^L}{l_s + l_t}, o\right\} = \frac{t^U - s^L}{l_s + l_t}$$

$$1 - Max\left\{\frac{t^U - s^L}{l_s + l_t}, o\right\} = 1 - \frac{t^U - s^L}{l_s + l_t} = \frac{s^U - t^L}{l_s + l_t} > 0$$

$$P\left(\mathbb{S} \ge \mathbb{T}\right) = \frac{s^U - t^L}{l_s + l_t}$$

Since $\frac{s^U - t^L}{l_s + l_t} > 0 \Rightarrow Max\left\{\frac{s^U - t^L}{l_s + l_t}, o\right\} = \frac{s^U - t^L}{l_s + l_t}$

$$1 - Max\left\{\frac{s^U - t^L}{l_s + l_t}, o\right\} = 1 - \frac{s^U - t^L}{l_s + l_t} = \frac{t^U - s^L}{l_s + l_t} > 0$$

$$P\left(\mathbb{S} \le \mathbb{T}\right) = \frac{t^U - s^L}{l_s + l_t}$$

Since $t^U - s^L = s^U - t^L \Rightarrow P\left(\mathbb{S} \ge \mathbb{T}\right) = P\left(\mathbb{S} \le \mathbb{T}\right)$ □

Proposition 2.2.4. *Let* $(\mathcal{F}, X)$ *and* $(\mathcal{G}, Y)$ *be* $\mathcal{L} - \mathcal{IVHFSS}$, *where* $X, Y \subseteq \mathcal{P}$. *Then*

$(\mathcal{H}, Z) = (\mathcal{F}, X) \cup (\mathcal{G}, Y)$ *is* $\mathcal{L} - \mathcal{IVHFSS}$ *if* $\breve{\delta} \in X$ *or* $\breve{\delta} \in Y$.

Proof. Let $(\mathcal{F}, X)$ and $(\mathcal{G}, Y)$ be $\mathcal{L} - \mathcal{IVHFSS}$ over U, where $X \subseteq \mathcal{P}$ and $Y \subseteq \mathcal{P}$.

Then $(\mathcal{H}, Z) = (\mathcal{F}, X) \cup (\mathcal{G}, Y)$, where $Z = X \cup Y$. Hence

$$h\left(\mathcal{H}\left(\breve{\delta}\right)\right) = \begin{cases} h\left(\mathcal{F}\left(\breve{\delta}\right)\right) & \text{if } \breve{\delta} \in X - Y \\ h\left(\mathcal{G}\left(\breve{\delta}\right)\right) & \text{if } \breve{\delta} \in Y - X \\ h\left(\mathcal{F}\left(\breve{\delta}\right)\right) \cup h\left(\mathcal{G}\left(\breve{\delta}\right)\right) & \text{if } e \in X \cap Y \end{cases}$$

Let $\breve{\delta}_i, \breve{\delta}_j \in Z$ such that $\breve{\delta}_i \preceq \breve{\delta}_j$.

Then $\breve{\delta}_i, \breve{\delta}_j \in X \cup Y$

$\Rightarrow \breve{\delta}_i \in X \cup Y$ and $\breve{\delta}_j \in X \cup Y$

$\Rightarrow \breve{\delta}_i \in X, \breve{\delta}_i \in Y$ and $\breve{\delta}_j \in X, \breve{\delta}_j \in Y.$

Case 1:

$\breve{\delta}_i \in X, \breve{\delta}_j \in X$

$$h\left(\mathcal{H}\left(\breve{\delta}_i\right)\right) = h\left(\mathcal{F}\left(\breve{\delta}_i\right)\right) \text{ and } h\left(\mathcal{H}\left(\breve{\delta}_j\right)\right) = h\left(\mathcal{F}\left(\breve{\delta}_j\right)\right).$$

Since $(\mathcal{F}, X)$ is $\mathcal{L} - \mathcal{IVHFSS}.$

$\Rightarrow \mathcal{F}\left(\breve{\delta}_i\right) \subseteq \mathcal{F}\left(\breve{\delta}_j\right)$

$\Rightarrow s\left(h_{\mathcal{F}}\left(\breve{\delta}_i\right)\right) \subseteq s\left(h_{\mathcal{F}}\left(\breve{\delta}_j\right)\right)$

$\Rightarrow s\left(h_{\mathcal{H}}\left(\breve{\delta}_i\right)\right) \subseteq s\left(h_{\mathcal{H}}\left(\breve{\delta}_j\right)\right).$

Then $\mathcal{H}\left(\breve{\delta}_i\right) \subseteq \mathcal{H}\left(\breve{\delta}_j\right)$

$\Rightarrow (\mathcal{H}, Z)$ is $\mathcal{L} - \mathcal{IVHFSS}.$

Case 2:

$\breve{\delta}_i \in Y, \breve{\delta}_j \in Y$

$$h\left(\mathcal{H}\left(\breve{\delta}_i\right)\right) = h\left(\mathcal{G}\left(\breve{\delta}_i\right)\right) \text{ and } h\left(\mathcal{H}\left(\breve{\delta}_j\right)\right) = h\left(\mathcal{G}\left(\breve{\delta}_j\right)\right).$$

Since $(\mathcal{G}, Y)$ is $\mathcal{L} - \mathcal{IVHFSS}$.

$$\Rightarrow \mathcal{G}\left(\breve{\delta}_i\right) \subseteq \mathcal{G}\left(\breve{\delta}_j\right)$$

$$\Rightarrow s\left(h_{\mathcal{G}}\left(\breve{\delta}_i\right)\right) \subseteq s\left(h_{\mathcal{G}}\left(\breve{\delta}_j\right)\right)$$

$$\Rightarrow s\left(h_{\mathcal{H}}\left(\breve{\delta}_i\right)\right) \subseteq s\left(h_{\mathcal{H}}\left(\breve{\delta}_j\right)\right).$$

$$\Rightarrow \text{Then } \mathcal{H}\left(\breve{\delta}_i\right) \subseteq \mathcal{H}\left(\breve{\delta}_j\right)$$

$$\Rightarrow (\mathcal{H}, Z) \text{ is } \mathcal{L} - \mathcal{IVHFSS}. \qquad \square$$

Result 2.2.5. *Let $X, Y \subseteq \mathcal{P}$. If $(\mathcal{F}, X)$ and $(\mathcal{G}, Y)$ are $\mathcal{L} - \mathcal{IVHFSS}$, then its union need not be $\mathcal{L} - \mathcal{IVHFSS}$ if $\breve{\delta} \in X \cap Y$.*

Example 1.

Let $U = \{\varrho_1, \varrho_2\}$ represents petrol and diesel and $\mathcal{P} = \{\breve{\delta}_1, \breve{\delta}_2, \breve{\delta}_3, \breve{\delta}_4, \breve{\delta}_5\}$ represents the years 2015, 2016, 2017, 2018 and 2019 respectively.

Let $X = \{\breve{\delta}_1, \breve{\delta}_2, \breve{\delta}_3\}, Y = \{\breve{\delta}_3, \breve{\delta}_4\}$. Then $Z = X \cup Y = \{\breve{\delta}_1, \breve{\delta}_2, \breve{\delta}_3, \breve{\delta}_4\}$.

Since $(\mathcal{F}, X)$ is a $\mathcal{L} - \mathcal{IVHFSS}$ which represents the changes in the requirement of petrol and diesel for the country in the respective years by one survey as follows,

$$(\mathcal{F}, X) = \{\mathcal{F}\left(\breve{\delta}_1\right) = \{< \varrho_1, \{[0.1, 0.3], [0.2, 0.4]\} >, < \varrho_2, \{[0.2, 0.4], [0.2, 0.3]\} >\},$$

$$\mathcal{F}\left(\breve{\delta}_2\right) = \{< \varrho_1, \{[0.3, 0.4], [0.3, 0.5]\} >, < \varrho_2, \{[0.1, 0.4], [0.4, 0.7]\} >\},$$

$\mathcal{F}\left(\breve{\delta}_3\right) = \{<\varrho_1, \{[0.41, 0.52], [0.41, 0.52]\} >, < \varrho_2, \{[0.42, 0.65], [0.42, 0.65]\} >\}\}.$

$(\mathcal{G}, Y) = \{\mathcal{G}\left(\breve{\delta}_3\right) = \{<\varrho_1, \{[0.2, 0.52], [0.2, 0.52]\} >, < \varrho_2, \{[0.3, 0.6], [0.3, 0.6]\} > \}, \mathcal{G}\left(\breve{\delta}_4\right) = \{<\varrho_1, \{[0.3, 0.6], [0.3, 0.6]\} >, < \varrho_2, \{[0.4, 0.5], [0.4, 0.5]\} >\}\}$ repre-

sents the requiremnet of petrol and diesel in the years 2017 and 2018 respectively by

another survey is $\mathcal{L} - \mathcal{IVHFSS}$. But by combining these two survey results, we get,

$(\mathcal{H}, Z) = \{\mathcal{H}\left(\breve{\delta}_1\right) = \{<\varrho_1, \{[0.1, 0.3], [0.2, 0.4]\} >, < \varrho_2, \{[0.2, 0.4], [0.2, 0.3]\} >\},$

$\mathcal{H}\left(\breve{\delta}_2\right) = \{<\varrho_1, \{[0.3, 0.4], [0.3, 0.5]\} >, < \varrho_2, \{[0.1, 0.4], [0.4, 0.7]\} >\},$

$\mathcal{H}\left(\breve{\delta}_3\right) = \{<\varrho_1, \{[0.1, 0.5], [0.1, 0.5]\} >, < \varrho_2, \{[0.4, 0.6], [0.4, 0.6]\} >\},$

$\mathcal{H}\left(\breve{\delta}_4\right) = \{<\varrho_1, \{[0.3, 0.6], [0.3, 0.6]\} >, < \varrho_2, \{[0.4, 0.5], [0.4, 0.5]\} >\}$ which rep-

resents the change in the requirement of petrol and diesel in the years 2015, 2016, 2017

and 2018 is not $\mathcal{L} - \mathcal{IVHFSS}$.

Result 2.2.6. *If* $(\mathcal{F}, X)$ *and* $(\mathcal{G}, Y)$ *are* $\mathcal{L} - \mathcal{IVHFSS}s$, *where* $X, Y \subseteq \mathcal{P}$. *Then*

$(\mathcal{H}, Z) = (\mathcal{H}, X) \cup (\mathcal{G}, Y)$ *need not be* $\mathcal{L} - \mathcal{IVHFSS}$ *if* $\breve{\delta}_i \in X$ *and* $\breve{\delta}_j \in Y, \forall i \neq j$.

Example 2.

Let $U = \{\varrho_1, \varrho_2\}$ bike and car respectively and $\mathcal{P} = \{\breve{\delta}_1, \breve{\delta}_2, \breve{\delta}_3, \breve{\delta}_4, \breve{\delta}_5\}$ represents the

years 2013, 2014, 2015, 2016 and 2017 respectively.

Let $X = \{\breve{\delta}_1, \breve{\delta}_2\}, Y = \{\breve{\delta}_3\}$. Then $Z = \{\breve{\delta}_1, \breve{\delta}_2, \breve{\delta}_3\}$.

Now $(\mathcal{F}, X)$ is a $\mathcal{L} - \mathcal{IVHFSS}$ which represents the most saled and most favourite

bike and car given by the two decision makers in the specific years as,

$(\mathcal{F}, X) = \{\mathcal{F}\left(\breve{\delta}_1\right) = \{< \varrho_1, \{[0.1, 0.3], [0.2, 0.4]\} >, < \varrho_2, \{[0.2, 0.4], [0.2, 0.3]\} >\},$

$\mathcal{F}\left(\breve{\delta}_2\right) = \{< \varrho_1, \{[0.3, 0.4], [0.3, 0.5]\} >, < \varrho_2, \{[0.1, 0.4], [0.4, 0.7]\} >\}\}.$

Also $(\mathcal{G}, Y) = \{\mathcal{G}\left(\breve{\delta}_3\right) = \{< \varrho_1, \{[0.2, 0.5], [0.2, 0.5]\} >, < \varrho_2, \{[0.3, 0.6], [0.3, 0.6]\} >$

$\}\}$ represents the most saled and most favourite bike and car given by the two de-

cision makers in the year 2015 is $\mathcal{L} - \mathcal{IVHFSS}$.But from these two sets we get,

$(\mathcal{H}, Z) = \{\mathcal{H}\left(\breve{\delta}_1\right) = \{< \varrho_1, \{[0.1, 0.3], [0.2, 0.4]\} >, < \varrho_2, \{[0.2, 0.4], [0.2, 0.3]\} >$

$\}, \mathcal{H}\left(\breve{\delta}_2\right) = \{< \varrho_1, \{[0.3, 0.4], [0.3, 0.5]\} >, < \varrho_2, \{[0.1, 0.4], [0.4, 0.7]\} >\},$

$\mathcal{H}\left(\breve{\delta}_3\right) = \{< \varrho_1, \{[0.2, 0.5], [0.2, 0.5]\} >, < \varrho_2, \{[0.3, 0.6], [0.3, 0.6]\} >\}\}$ which is

not $\mathcal{L} - \mathcal{IVHFSS}$.

Result 2.2.7. *If $(\mathcal{F}, X)$ and $(\mathcal{G}, Y)$ are $\mathcal{L} - \mathcal{IVHFSS}$, where $X \subseteq \mathcal{P}$ and $Y \subseteq \mathcal{P}$,*

then its intersection need not be $\mathcal{L} - \mathcal{IVHFSS}$.

Example 3.

Let $U = \{\varrho_1, \varrho_2\}$ represents bike and car and $\mathcal{P} = \{\breve{\delta}_1, \breve{\delta}_2, \breve{\delta}_3, \breve{\delta}_4, \breve{\delta}_5\}$ represents the years 2013, 2014, 2015, 2016 and 2017 respectively.

Let $X = \{\breve{\delta}_1, \breve{\delta}_2, \breve{\delta}_3, \breve{\delta}_4\}, Y = \{\breve{\delta}_3, \breve{\delta}_4\}$. Then $Z = X \cap Y = \{\breve{\delta}_3, \breve{\delta}_4\}$.

Since $(\mathcal{F}, X)$ is a $\mathcal{L} - \mathcal{IVHFSS}$ which represents most saled and most favourite bike

and car given by two decision makers in the respective years by ,

$(\mathcal{F}, X) = \{\mathcal{F}\left(\breve{\delta}_1\right) = \{< \varrho_1, \{[0.1, 0.3], [0.2, 0.4]\} >, < \varrho_2, \{[0.2, 0.4], [0.2, 0.3]\} >\},$

$\mathcal{F}\left(\breve{\delta}_2\right) = \{< \varrho_1, \{[0.3, 0.4], [0.3, 0.5]\} >, < \varrho_2, \{[0.1, 0.4], [0.4, 0.7]\} >\},$

$\mathcal{F}\left(\breve{\delta}_3\right) = \{< \varrho_1, \{[0.4, 0.5], [0.4, 0.5]\} >, < \varrho_2, \{[0.4, 0.6], [0.4, 0.6]\} >\},$

$\mathcal{F}\left(\breve{\delta}_4\right) = \{< \varrho_1, \{[0.5, 0.6], [0.5, 0.6]\} >, < \varrho_2, \{[0.5, 0.6], [0.5, 0.6]\} >\}\}.$

$(\mathcal{G}, Y) = \{\mathcal{G}\left(\breve{\delta}_3\right) = \{< \varrho_1, \{[0.2, 0.5], [0.2, 0.5]\} >, < \varrho_2, \{[0.3, 0.6], [0.3, 0.6]\} >$

$\}, \mathcal{G}\left(\breve{\delta}_4\right) = \{< \varrho_1, \{[0.4, 0.6], [0.4, 0.6]\} >, < \varrho_2, \{[0.2, 0.5], [0.2, 0.5]\} >\}\}$ is

$\mathcal{L} - \mathcal{IVHFSS}.$

But $(\mathcal{H}, Z) = \{\mathcal{H}\left(\breve{\delta}_3\right) = \{< \varrho_1, \{[0.2, 0.5], [0.2, 0.5]\} >, < \varrho_2, \{[0.3, 0.6], [0.3, 0.6]\} >$

$\}, \mathcal{H}\left(\breve{\delta}_4\right) = \{< \varrho_1, \{[0.4, 0.6], [0.4, 0.6]\} >, < \varrho_2, \{[0.2, 0.5], [0.2, 0.5]\} >\}$ is not

$\mathcal{L} - \mathcal{IVHFSS}.$

Result 2.2.8. *If* $(\mathcal{F}, X)$ *is* $\mathcal{L} - \mathcal{IVHFSS}$, *then* $(\mathcal{F}^c, X)$ *need not be*

$\mathcal{L} - \mathcal{IVHFSS}.$

Example 4.

Let $U = \{\varrho_1, \varrho_2\}$ and $\mathcal{P} = \{\breve{\delta}_1, \breve{\delta}_2, \breve{\delta}_3\}$, where $\breve{\delta}_1 \preceq \breve{\delta}_2 \preceq \breve{\delta}_3$

Consider the $\mathcal{L} - \mathcal{IVHFSS}$

$(\mathcal{F}, P) = \{\mathcal{F}\left(\breve{\delta}_1\right) = \{< \varrho_1, \{[0.1, 0.3], [0.2, 0.4]\} >, < \varrho_2, \{[0.2, 0.4], [0.2, 0.3]\} >\},$

$\mathcal{F}\left(\breve{\delta}_2\right) = \{< \varrho_1, \{[0.3, 0.4], [0.3, 0.5]\} >, < \varrho_2, \{[0.1, 0.4], [0.4, 0.7]\} >\},$

$\mathcal{F}\left(\breve{\delta}_3\right) = \{< \varrho_1, \{[0.4, 0.5], [0.45, 0.6]\} >, < \varrho_2, \{[0.4, 0.6], [0.4, 0.6]\} >\}$

But $(\mathcal{F}^c, P) = \{\mathcal{F}^c\left(\breve{\delta}_1\right) = \{< \varrho_1, \{[0.7, 0.9], [0.6, 0.8]\} >, < \varrho_2, \{[0.6, 0.8], [0.7, 0.8]\} >$

$\}, \mathcal{F}^c\left(\breve{\delta}_2\right) = \{< \varrho_1, \{[0.6, 0.7], [0.5, 0.7]\} >, < \varrho_2, \{[0.6, 0.9], [0.3, 0.6]\} >\},$

$\mathcal{F}^c\left(\breve{\delta}_3\right) = \{< \varrho_1, \{[0.5, 0.6], [0.4, 0.55]\} >, < \varrho_2, \{[0.4, 0.6], [0.4, 0.6]\} >\}$

is not $\mathcal{L} - \mathcal{IVHFSS}$.

Chapter 3

Morphisms on Lattice Ordered Interval-Valued Hesitant Fuzzy Soft Sets

In this section, the notion of $\mathcal{L}-$Isomorphism and $\mathcal{L}-$Homomorphism has been initiated and discussed with example.

3.1 $\mathcal{L}-$Isomorphism and $\mathcal{L}-$Homomorphism

Definition 3.1.1. *Let* $(\mathcal{F},\mathcal{P})$ *and* $(\mathcal{G},\mathcal{P})$ *be* $\mathcal{L}-\mathcal{IVHFSS}$ *over* U. *Let* $S\,(\mathcal{F})$ *and* $S\,(\mathcal{G})$ *be the set of all score functions of* $(\mathcal{F},\mathcal{P})$ *and* $(\mathcal{G},\mathcal{P})$ *respectively.* *If a map* $\varphi\colon S\,(\mathcal{F})\to S\,(\mathcal{G})$ *is 1-1, onto and* $s\left(h_{\mathcal{F}}\left(\breve{\delta}_i\right)\right)\subseteq s\left(h_{\mathcal{F}}\left(\breve{\delta}_j\right)\right)\Leftrightarrow\varphi[s\left(h_{\mathcal{F}}\left(\breve{\delta}_i\right)\right)]\subseteq\varphi[s\left(h_{\mathcal{F}}\left(\breve{\delta}_j\right)\right)]$, *then* φ *is called as* $\mathcal{L}-$*isomorphism.* *In this case we say that* $(\mathcal{F},\mathcal{P})$ *and* $(\mathcal{G},\mathcal{P})$ *are* $\mathcal{L}-$*isomorphic and is denoted by* $(\mathcal{F},\mathcal{P})\approx(\mathcal{G},\mathcal{P})$.

[1]Journal of Intelligent & Fuzzy Systems, IOS Press

Example 1.

Let $U = \{x_1, x_2\}$ represents bike, car respectively and $\mathcal{P} = \{\breve{\delta}_1, \breve{\delta}_2, \breve{\delta}_3\}$ represents the

years 2014, 2015 and 2016 respectively. Then an $\mathcal{L} - \mathcal{IVHFSS}$ $(\mathcal{F}, \mathcal{P}) = \{\mathcal{F}\left(\breve{\delta}_1\right) =$

$\{< x_1, [0.1, 0.3], [0.2, 0.4] >, < x_2, [0.2, 0.4], [0.2, 0.3] >\}$,

$\mathcal{F}\left(\breve{\delta}_2\right) = \{< x_1, [0.3, 0.4], [0.3, 0.5] >, < x_2, [0.1, 0.4], [0.4, 0.7] >\}$,

$\mathcal{F}\left(\breve{\delta}_3\right) = \{< x_1, [0.4, 0.5], [0.4, 0.5] >, < x_2, [0.4, 0.6], [0.4, 0.6] >\}\}$ represents the

changes occurred in the price of bike and car calculated on half yearly for every year.

Also an $\mathcal{L} - \mathcal{IVHFSS}$ $(\mathcal{G}, \mathcal{P}) = \{\mathcal{G}\left(\breve{\delta}_1\right) = \{< x_1, [0.05, 0.15], [0.1, 0.2] >,$

$< x_2, [0.1, 0.2], [0.1, 0.15] >\}, \mathcal{G}\left(\breve{\delta}_2\right) = \{< x_1, [0.15, 0.2], [0.1, 0.25] >,$

$< x_2, [0.05, 0.2], [0.2, 0.35] >\}, \mathcal{G}\left(\breve{\delta}_3\right) = \{< x_1, [0.2, 0.25], [0.2, 0.25] >,$

$< x_2, [0.2, 0.3], [0.2, 0.3] >\}\}$ represents the changes occurred in the sales of bike and

car calculated on half yearly for every year.

Define a map $\varphi: S\left(\mathcal{F}\right) \to S\left(\mathcal{G}\right)$ by $\varphi\left(s\left(h_{\mathcal{F}}\left(\breve{\delta}_i\right)\right)\right) = \frac{s\left(h_{\mathcal{F}}\left(\breve{\delta}_i\right)\right)}{2}, \forall i.$

Claim:φ is 1-1 and onto.

For 1-1:

Suppose $\breve{\delta}_i, \breve{\delta}_j \in \mathcal{P}$ with $\breve{\delta}_i \neq \breve{\delta}_j$

$\Rightarrow \breve{\delta}_i \preceq \breve{\delta}_j$ or $\breve{\delta}_i > \breve{\delta}_j$

$\Rightarrow \mathcal{F}\left(\breve{\delta}_i\right) \subset \mathcal{F}\left(\breve{\delta}_j\right)$ or $\mathcal{F}\left(\breve{\delta}_i\right) \supset \mathcal{F}\left(\breve{\delta}_j\right)$,

Since $(\mathcal{F}, \mathcal{P})$ is $\mathcal{L} - \mathcal{IVHFSS}$.

$\Rightarrow s\left(h_{\mathcal{F}}\left(\breve{\delta}_i\right)\right) \subset s\left(h_{\mathcal{F}}\left(\breve{\delta}_j\right)\right)$ or $s\left(h_{\mathcal{F}}\left(\breve{\delta}_i\right)\right) \supset s\left(h_{\mathcal{F}}\left(\breve{\delta}_j\right)\right)$

$\Rightarrow s\left(h_{\mathcal{F}}\left(\breve{\delta}_i\right)\right) \neq s\left(h_{\mathcal{F}}\left(\breve{\delta}_j\right)\right)$

$\Rightarrow \frac{s\left(h_{\mathcal{F}}(\breve{\delta}_i)\right)}{2} \neq \frac{s\left(h_{\mathcal{F}}(\breve{\delta}_j)\right)}{2}$

$\Rightarrow \varphi$ is 1-1.

For onto:

$s\left(h_{\mathcal{G}1}\left(\breve{\delta}_1\right)\right) = \frac{[0.15,0.35]}{2} = [0.075, 0.175]$

$s\left(h_{\mathcal{F}1}\left(\breve{\delta}_1\right)\right) = \frac{[0.3,0.7]}{2} = [0.15, 0.35]$

$\Rightarrow \frac{s\left(h_{\mathcal{F}1}(\breve{\delta}_1)\right)}{2} = [0.075, 0.175]$

$\Rightarrow \varphi\left(s\left(h_{\mathcal{F}1}\left(\breve{\delta}_1\right)\right)\right) = \frac{s\left(h_{\mathcal{F}1}(\breve{\delta}_1)\right)}{2} = s\left(h_{\mathcal{G}1}\left(\breve{\delta}_1\right)\right) = [0.075, 0.175]$

$s\left(h_{\mathcal{G}1}\left(\breve{\delta}_2\right)\right) = \frac{[0.2,0.35]}{2} = [0.1, 0.175]$

$s\left(h_{\mathcal{F}1}\left(\breve{\delta}_2\right)\right) = \frac{[0.4,0.7]}{2} = [0.2, 0.35]$

$\Rightarrow \frac{s\left(h_{\mathcal{F}1}(\breve{\delta}_2)\right)}{2} = [0.1, 0.175]$

$\Rightarrow \varphi\left(s\left(h_{\mathcal{F}1}\left(\breve{\delta}_2\right)\right)\right) = \frac{s\left(h_{\mathcal{F}1}(\breve{\delta}_2)\right)}{2} = s\left(h_{\mathcal{G}1}\left(\breve{\delta}_2\right)\right) = [0.1, 0.175]$

Proceeding like this, we get for every $s\left(h_{\mathcal{G}}\left(\breve{\delta}_i\right)\right) \in S\left(\mathcal{G}\right)$, there exists $s\left(h_{\mathcal{F}}\left(\breve{\delta}_i\right)\right) \in S\left(\mathcal{F}\right)$ such that $\varphi\left(s\left(h_{\mathcal{F}}\left(\breve{\delta}_i\right)\right)\right) = s\left(h_{\mathcal{G}}\left(\breve{\delta}_i\right)\right)$

$\Rightarrow \varphi$ is onto.

Now $s\left(h_{\mathcal{F}1}\left(\breve{\delta}_1\right)\right) = \frac{[0.3,0.7]}{2} = [0.15, 0.35]$

$s\left(h_{\mathcal{F}2}\left(\breve{\delta}_1\right)\right) = \frac{[0.4,0.7]}{2} = [0.2, 0.35]$

$s\left(h_{\mathcal{F}1}\left(\breve{\delta}_2\right)\right) = \frac{[0.6,0.9]}{2} = [0.3, 0.45]$

$s\left(h_{\mathcal{F}2}\left(\breve{\delta}_2\right)\right) = \frac{[0.5,1.1]}{2} = [0.25, 0.55]$

$s\left(h_{\mathcal{F}1}\left(\breve{\delta}_3\right)\right) = \frac{[0.8,1]}{2} = [0.4, 0.5]$

$s\left(h_{\mathcal{F}2}\left(\breve{\delta}_3\right)\right) = \frac{[0.8,1.2]}{2} = [0.4, 0.6]$

$s\left(h_{\mathcal{G}1}\left(\breve{\delta}_1\right)\right) = \frac{[0.15,0.35]}{2} = [0.075, 0.175]$

$s\left(h_{\mathcal{G}2}\left(\breve{\delta}_1\right)\right) = \frac{[0.2,0.35]}{2} = [0.1, 0.175]$

$s\left(h_{\mathcal{G}1}\left(\breve{\delta}_2\right)\right) = \frac{[0.25,0.45]}{2} = [0.125, 0.225]$

$s\left(h_{\mathcal{G}2}\left(\breve{\delta}_2\right)\right) = \frac{[0.25,0.55]}{2} = [0.125, 0.275]$

$s\left(h_{\mathcal{G}1}\left(\breve{\delta}_3\right)\right) = \frac{[0.4,0.5]}{2} = [0.2, 0.25]$

$s\left(h_{\mathcal{G}2}\left(\breve{\delta}_3\right)\right) = \frac{[0.4,0.6]}{2} = [0.2, 0.3]$

Since $(\mathcal{F}, \mathcal{P})$ is $\mathcal{L} - \mathcal{IVHFSS}$

$$\Rightarrow s\left(h_{\mathcal{F}}\left(\breve{\delta}_i\right)\right) \subseteq s\left(h_{\mathcal{F}}\left(\breve{\delta}_j\right)\right)$$

Since $(\mathcal{G}, \mathcal{P})$ is $\mathcal{L} - \mathcal{IVHFSS}$

$$\Rightarrow s\left(h_{\mathcal{G}}\left(\breve{\delta}_i\right)\right) \subseteq s\left(h_{\mathcal{G}}\left(\breve{\delta}_j\right)\right)$$

$$\Rightarrow \varphi\left(s\left(h_{\mathcal{F}}\left(\breve{\delta}_i\right)\right)\right) = \frac{s\left(h_{\mathcal{F}}\left(\breve{\delta}_i\right)\right)}{2} = s\left(h_{\mathcal{G}}\left(\breve{\delta}_i\right)\right)$$

$$\Rightarrow s\left(h_{\mathcal{F}}\left(\breve{\delta}_i\right)\right) \subseteq s\left(h_{\mathcal{F}}\left(\breve{\delta}_j\right)\right) \Leftrightarrow$$

$$\varphi\left(s\left(h_{\mathcal{F}}\left(\breve{\delta}_i\right)\right)\right) \subseteq \varphi\left(s\left(h_{\mathcal{F}}\left(\breve{\delta}_j\right)\right)\right)$$

$$\Rightarrow \varphi \colon S(\mathcal{F}) \to S(\mathcal{G}) \text{ is } \mathcal{L}-\text{isomorphism.}$$

Definition 3.1.2. *Let $(\mathcal{F}, \mathcal{P})$ and $(\mathcal{G}, \mathcal{P})$ be $\mathcal{L} - \mathcal{IVHFSS}$ over U. Let $S(\mathcal{F})$ and $S(\mathcal{G})$ be the set of all score functions of $(\mathcal{F}, \mathcal{P})$ and $(\mathcal{G}, \mathcal{P})$ respectively. A map $\varphi \colon S(\mathcal{F}) \to S(\mathcal{G})$ is said to be a $\mathcal{L}-$homomorphism if*

(i) $\varphi\left(s\left(h_{\mathcal{F}}\left(\breve{\delta}_i\right)\right) \ddot{\vee} s\left(h_{\mathcal{F}}\left(\breve{\delta}_j\right)\right)\right) = \varphi\left(s\left(h_{\mathcal{F}}\left(\breve{\delta}_i\right)\right)\right) \ddot{\vee} \varphi\left(s\left(h_{\mathcal{F}}\left(\breve{\delta}_j\right)\right)\right)$

(ii) $\varphi\left(s\left(h_{\mathcal{F}}\left(\breve{\delta}_i\right)\right) \ddot{\wedge} s\left(h_{\mathcal{F}}\left(\breve{\delta}_j\right)\right)\right) = \varphi\left(s\left(h_{\mathcal{F}}\left(\breve{\delta}_i\right)\right)\right) \ddot{\wedge} \varphi\left(s\left(h_{\mathcal{F}}\left(\breve{\delta}_j\right)\right)\right)$

3.2 Main Results

In this section, the vital results of $\mathcal{L}-$homomorphism and $\mathcal{L}-$isomomorphism were discussed.

Proposition 3.2.1. *Let* $(\mathcal{F}, \mathcal{P})$ *and* $(\mathcal{G}, \mathcal{P})$ *be* $\mathcal{L} - \mathcal{IVHFSS}$ *over* U. *Let* $S(\mathcal{F})$ *and* $S(\mathcal{G})$ *be the set of all score functions of* $(\mathcal{F}, \mathcal{P})$ *and* $(\mathcal{G}, \mathcal{P})$ *respectively. If* $\varphi \colon S(\mathcal{F}) \to S(\mathcal{G})$ *is a* $\mathcal{L}-$*homomorphism with 1-1 and onto, then* φ *is an* $\mathcal{L}-$*isomorphism.*

Proof. Let $\varphi \colon S(\mathcal{F}) \to S(\mathcal{G})$ be a $\mathcal{L}-$homomorphism.

Let φ be 1-1 and onto.

Since φ is $\mathcal{L}-$homomorphism.

$$\Rightarrow \varphi \left(s \left(h_{\mathcal{F}} \left(\breve{\delta}_i \right) \right) \ddot{\vee} s \left(h_{\mathcal{F}} \left(\breve{\delta}_j \right) \right) \right) = \varphi \left(s \left(h_{\mathcal{F}} \left(\breve{\delta}_i \right) \right) \right) \ddot{\vee} \varphi \left(s \left(h_{\mathcal{F}} \left(\breve{\delta}_j \right) \right) \right) \to (1)$$

$$\varphi \left(s \left(h_{\mathcal{F}} \left(\breve{\delta}_i \right) \right) \ddot{\wedge} s \left(h_{\mathcal{F}} \left(\breve{\delta}_j \right) \right) \right) = \varphi \left(s \left(h_{\mathcal{F}} \left(\breve{\delta}_i \right) \right) \right) \ddot{\wedge} \varphi \left(s \left(h_{\mathcal{F}} \left(\breve{\delta}_j \right) \right) \right) \to (2)$$

Case 1.

Claim: $s \left(h_{\mathcal{F}} \left(\breve{\delta}_i \right) \right) \subseteq s \left(h_{\mathcal{F}} \left(\breve{\delta}_j \right) \right) \Leftrightarrow \varphi[s \left(h_{\mathcal{F}} \left(\breve{\delta}_i \right) \right)] \subseteq \varphi[s \left(h_{\mathcal{F}} \left(\breve{\delta}_j \right) \right)]$, by using

(1)

Suppose $s \left(h_{\mathcal{F}} \left(\breve{\delta}_i \right) \right) \subseteq s \left(h_{\mathcal{F}} \left(\breve{\delta}_j \right) \right) \Leftrightarrow s \left(h_{\mathcal{F}} \left(\breve{\delta}_i \right) \right) \ddot{\vee} s \left(h_{\mathcal{F}} \left(\breve{\delta}_j \right) \right) = s \left(h_{\mathcal{F}} \left(\breve{\delta}_j \right) \right)$

$$\Leftrightarrow \varphi \left(s \left(h_{\mathcal{F}} \left(\breve{\delta}_i \right) \right) \ddot{\vee} s \left(h_{\mathcal{F}} \left(\breve{\delta}_j \right) \right) \right) = \varphi \left(s \left(h_{\mathcal{F}} \left(\breve{\delta}_j \right) \right) \right) \to (3)$$

$$\Leftrightarrow \varphi \left(s \left(h_{\mathcal{F}} \left(\breve{\delta}_i \right) \right) \right) \ddot{\vee} \varphi \left(s \left(h_{\mathcal{F}} \left(\breve{\delta}_j \right) \right) \right) = \varphi \left(s \left(h_{\mathcal{F}} \left(\breve{\delta}_j \right) \right) \right), \text{by } (1),(3)$$

$$\Leftrightarrow \varphi \left(s \left(h_{\mathcal{F}} \left(\breve{\delta}_i \right) \right) \right) \subseteq \varphi \left(s \left(h_{\mathcal{F}} \left(\breve{\delta}_j \right) \right) \right)$$

$$\Rightarrow s \left(h_{\mathcal{F}} \left(\breve{\delta}_i \right) \right) \subseteq s \left(h_{\mathcal{F}} \left(\breve{\delta}_j \right) \right) \Leftrightarrow \varphi \left(s \left(h_{\mathcal{F}} \left(\breve{\delta}_i \right) \right) \right) \subseteq \varphi \left(s \left(h_{\mathcal{F}} \left(\breve{\delta}_j \right) \right) \right)$$

Case 2.

Claim: $s\left(h_{\mathcal{F}}\left(\breve{\delta}_i\right)\right) \subseteq s\left(h_{\mathcal{F}}\left(\breve{\delta}_j\right)\right) \Leftrightarrow \varphi[s\left(h_{\mathcal{F}}\left(\breve{\delta}_i\right)\right)] \subseteq \varphi[s\left(h_{\mathcal{F}}\left(\breve{\delta}_j\right)\right)]$, by using

(2)

Suppose $s\left(h_{\mathcal{F}}\left(\breve{\delta}_i\right)\right) \subseteq s\left(h_{\mathcal{F}}\left(\breve{\delta}_j\right)\right) \Leftrightarrow s\left(h_{\mathcal{F}}\left(\breve{\delta}_i\right)\right) \ddot{\wedge} s\left(h_{\mathcal{F}}\left(\breve{\delta}_j\right)\right) = s\left(h_{\mathcal{F}}\left(\breve{\delta}_i\right)\right)$

$\Leftrightarrow \varphi\left(s\left(h_{\mathcal{F}}\left(\breve{\delta}_i\right)\right) \ddot{\wedge} s\left(h_{\mathcal{F}}\left(\breve{\delta}_j\right)\right)\right) = \varphi\left(s\left(h_{\mathcal{F}}\left(\breve{\delta}_i\right)\right)\right) \rightarrow (3)$

$\Leftrightarrow \varphi\left(s\left(h_{\mathcal{F}}\left(\breve{\delta}_i\right)\right)\right) \ddot{\wedge} \varphi\left(s\left(h_{\mathcal{F}}\left(\breve{\delta}_j\right)\right)\right) = \varphi\left(s\left(h_{\mathcal{F}}\left(\breve{\delta}_i\right)\right)\right)$, by $(2),(3)$

$\Leftrightarrow \varphi\left(s\left(h_{\mathcal{F}}\left(\breve{\delta}_i\right)\right)\right) \subseteq \varphi\left(s\left(h_{\mathcal{F}}\left(\breve{\delta}_j\right)\right)\right)$

$\Rightarrow s\left(h_{\mathcal{F}}\left(\breve{\delta}_i\right)\right) \subseteq s\left(h_{\mathcal{F}}\left(\breve{\delta}_j\right)\right) \Leftrightarrow \varphi\left(s\left(h_{\mathcal{F}}\left(\breve{\delta}_i\right)\right)\right) \subseteq \varphi\left(s\left(h_{\mathcal{F}}\left(\breve{\delta}_j\right)\right)\right).$ $\qquad \square$

Proposition 3.2.2. *Let $(\mathcal{F},\mathcal{P})$ and $(\mathcal{G},\mathcal{P})$ be $\mathcal{L}-\mathcal{IVHFSS}$ over U. Let $S(\mathcal{F})$ and $S(\mathcal{G})$ be the set of all score functions of $(\mathcal{F},\mathcal{P})$ and $(\mathcal{G},\mathcal{P})$ respectively. If $\varphi \colon S(\mathcal{F}) \to S(\mathcal{G})$ is onto $\mathcal{L}-$homomorphism, then the least element of $S(\mathcal{F})$ maps to the least element of $S(\mathcal{G})$.*

Proof. Let $(\mathcal{F},\mathcal{P}),(\mathcal{G},\mathcal{P})$ be $\mathcal{L}-\mathcal{IVHFSS}$ over U. Let $S(\mathcal{F})$ and $S(\mathcal{G})$ denotes the set of all score functions of $(\mathcal{F},\mathcal{P})$ and $(\mathcal{G},\mathcal{P})$ respectively.

Suppose $s\left(h_{\mathcal{F}}\left(\breve{\delta}_i\right)\right)$ is the least element in $S(\mathcal{F})$

$\Rightarrow s\left(h_{\mathcal{F}}\left(\breve{\delta}_i\right)\right) \subset s\left(h_{\mathcal{F}}\left(\breve{\delta}_j\right)\right), \forall j$

$$\Rightarrow s\left(h_{\mathcal{F}}\left(\breve{\delta}_i\right)\right) \check{\vee} s\left(h_{\mathcal{F}}\left(\breve{\delta}_j\right)\right) = s\left(h_{\mathcal{F}}\left(\breve{\delta}_j\right)\right)$$

$$\Rightarrow \varphi\left(s\left(h_{\mathcal{F}}\left(\breve{\delta}_i\right)\right) \check{\vee} s\left(h_{\mathcal{F}}\left(\breve{\delta}_j\right)\right)\right) = \varphi\left(s\left(h_{\mathcal{F}}\left(\breve{\delta}_j\right)\right)\right)$$

$$\Rightarrow \varphi\left(s\left(h_{\mathcal{F}}\left(\breve{\delta}_i\right)\right)\right) \check{\vee} \varphi\left(s\left(h_{\mathcal{F}}\left(\breve{\delta}_j\right)\right)\right) = \varphi\left(s\left(h_{\mathcal{F}}\left(\breve{\delta}_j\right)\right)\right),$$

Since φ is $\mathcal{L}$−homomorphism.

$$\Rightarrow \varphi\left(s\left(h_{\mathcal{F}}\left(\breve{\delta}_i\right)\right)\right) \subset \varphi\left(s\left(h_{\mathcal{F}}\left(\breve{\delta}_j\right)\right)\right), \forall j \rightarrow (1)$$

Since φ is onto. Then there exists $s\left(h_{\mathcal{G}}\left(\breve{\delta}_i\right)\right), s\left(h_{\mathcal{G}}\left(\breve{\delta}_j\right)\right) \in S\left(\mathcal{G}\right)$ such that

$$\varphi\left(s\left(h_{\mathcal{F}}\left(\breve{\delta}_i\right)\right)\right) = s\left(h_{\mathcal{G}}\left(\breve{\delta}_i\right)\right) \text{ and } \varphi\left(s\left(h_{\mathcal{F}}\left(\breve{\delta}_j\right)\right)\right) = s\left(h_{\mathcal{G}}\left(\breve{\delta}_j\right)\right) \rightarrow (2)$$

From $(1), (2)$, we have $s\left(h_{\mathcal{G}}\left(\breve{\delta}_i\right)\right) \subset s\left(h_{\mathcal{G}}\left(\breve{\delta}_j\right)\right), \forall j$

$$\Rightarrow \varphi\left(s\left(h_{\mathcal{F}}\left(\breve{\delta}_i\right)\right)\right) = s\left(h_{\mathcal{G}}\left(\breve{\delta}_i\right)\right) \text{ is the least element in } S\left(\mathcal{G}\right). \qquad \square$$

Proposition 3.2.3. *Let $(\mathcal{F}, \mathcal{P})$ and $(\mathcal{G}, \mathcal{P})$ be $\mathcal{L} - \mathcal{IVHFSS}$ over U. Let $S\left(\mathcal{F}\right)$ and $S\left(\mathcal{G}\right)$ be the set of all score functions of $(\mathcal{F}, \mathcal{P})$ and $(\mathcal{G}, \mathcal{P})$ respectively. If $\varphi \colon S\left(\mathcal{F}\right) \rightarrow S\left(\mathcal{G}\right)$ is onto $\mathcal{L}$−homomorphism and $s\left(h_{\mathcal{G}}\left(\breve{\delta}_i\right)\right), s\left(h_{\mathcal{G}}\left(\breve{\delta}_j\right)\right) \in S\left(\mathcal{G}\right)$ such that $s\left(h_{\mathcal{G}}\left(\breve{\delta}_i\right)\right) \subset s\left(h_{\mathcal{G}}\left(\breve{\delta}_j\right)\right)$, then there exists $s\left(h_{\mathcal{F}}\left(\breve{\delta}_i\right)\right), s\left(h_{\mathcal{F}}\left(\breve{\delta}_j\right)\right) \in S\left(\mathcal{F}\right)$ such that $\varphi\left(s\left(h_{\mathcal{F}}\left(\breve{\delta}_i\right)\right)\right) = s\left(h_{\mathcal{G}}\left(\breve{\delta}_i\right)\right), \varphi\left(s\left(h_{\mathcal{F}}\left(\breve{\delta}_j\right)\right)\right) = s\left(h_{\mathcal{G}}\left(\breve{\delta}_j\right)\right)$ and $s\left(h_{\mathcal{F}}\left(\breve{\delta}_i\right)\right) \subset s\left(h_{\mathcal{F}}\left(\breve{\delta}_j\right)\right)$*

Proof. Let $\varphi \colon S\left(\mathcal{F}\right) \rightarrow S\left(\mathcal{G}\right)$ be onto $\mathcal{L}$−homomorphism. Suppose $s\left(h_{\mathcal{G}}\left(\breve{\delta}_i\right)\right),$

$s\left(h_{\mathcal{G}}\left(\breve{\delta}_j\right)\right) \in S\left(\mathcal{G}\right)$ such that $s\left(h_{\mathcal{G}}\left(\breve{\delta}_i\right)\right) \subset s\left(h_{\mathcal{G}}\left(\breve{\delta}_j\right)\right) \rightarrow (1)$.

Since φ is onto. Then there exists $s\left(h_{\mathcal{F}}\left(\breve{\delta}_i\right)\right), s\left(h_{\mathcal{F}}\left(\breve{\delta}_j\right)\right) \in S\left(\mathcal{F}\right)$ such that

$$\varphi\left(s\left(h_{\mathcal{F}}\left(\breve{\delta}_i\right)\right)\right) = s\left(h_{\mathcal{G}}\left(\breve{\delta}_i\right)\right), \varphi\left(s\left(h_{\mathcal{F}}\left(\breve{\delta}_j\right)\right)\right) = s\left(h_{\mathcal{G}}\left(\breve{\delta}_j\right)\right) \rightarrow (2).$$

Claim: $s\left(h_{\mathcal{F}}\left(\breve{\delta}_i\right)\right) \subset s\left(h_{\mathcal{F}}\left(\breve{\delta}_j\right)\right)$

Since φ is $\mathcal{L}-$homomorphism.

$$\varphi\left(s\left(h_{\mathcal{F}}\left(\breve{\delta}_i\right)\right) \check{\vee} s\left(h_{\mathcal{F}}\left(\breve{\delta}_j\right)\right)\right)$$

$$= \varphi\left(s\left(h_{\mathcal{F}}\left(\breve{\delta}_i\right)\right)\right) \check{\vee} \varphi\left(s\left(h_{\mathcal{F}}\left(\breve{\delta}_j\right)\right)\right)$$

$$= s\left(h_{\mathcal{G}}\left(\breve{\delta}_i\right)\right) \check{\vee} s\left(h_{\mathcal{G}}\left(\breve{\delta}_j\right)\right), by\,(2)$$

$$= s\left(h_{\mathcal{G}}\left(\breve{\delta}_j\right)\right) \rightarrow (3), by\,(1)$$

Now suppose $s\left(h_{\mathcal{F}}\left(\breve{\delta}_i\right)\right) \check{\vee} s\left(h_{\mathcal{F}}\left(\breve{\delta}_j\right)\right) = s\left(h_{\mathcal{F}}\left(\breve{\delta}_i\right)\right)$

$$\Rightarrow \varphi\left(s\left(h_{\mathcal{F}}\left(\breve{\delta}_i\right)\right) \check{\vee} s\left(h_{\mathcal{F}}\left(\breve{\delta}_j\right)\right)\right) = \varphi\left(s\left(h_{\mathcal{F}}\left(\breve{\delta}_i\right)\right)\right)$$

$$= s\left(h_{\mathcal{G}}\left(\breve{\delta}_i\right)\right), by\,(2)$$ which is a contradiction to (3).

Thus $s\left(h_{\mathcal{F}}\left(\breve{\delta}_i\right)\right) \check{\vee} s\left(h_{\mathcal{F}}\left(\breve{\delta}_j\right)\right) = s\left(h_{\mathcal{F}}\left(\breve{\delta}_j\right)\right)$

$$\Rightarrow s\left(h_{\mathcal{F}}\left(\breve{\delta}_i\right)\right) \subset s\left(h_{\mathcal{F}}\left(\breve{\delta}_j\right)\right). \qquad \square$$

❖❖❖❖❖❖❖

Chapter 4

Duality in L-IVHFSS and Contra-L-IVHFSS

In this chapter, the conception duality in IVHFSS was described and the Contra-$\mathcal{L} - \mathcal{IVHFSS}$ was introduced. Also the impact of duality in $\mathcal{L} - \mathcal{IVHFSS}$ and Contra-$\mathcal{L} - \mathcal{IVHFSS}$ was investigated.

4.1 Duality in L-IVHFSS and Contra-L-IVHFSS

Definition 4.1.1. *Let $\mathcal{P}$ and $\mathcal{Q}$ be parameter sets. Let $(\mathcal{F}, \mathcal{P})$ be an IVHFSS over* U. *A dual of $(\mathcal{F}, \mathcal{P})$ is defined as an IVHFSS $(\mathcal{F}, \mathcal{Q})$ if $\mathcal{F}\left(\breve{\delta}_i\right) \subseteq \mathcal{F}\left(\breve{\delta}_j\right) \Leftrightarrow \mathcal{F}(\breve{\varepsilon}_i) \supseteq \mathcal{F}(\breve{\varepsilon}_j), \forall \varrho \in$ U.*

Definition 4.1.2. *Let $(\mathcal{F}, \mathcal{P})$ be an IVHFSS over* U. *If $\mathcal{F}(\breve{\varepsilon}_i) \supseteq \mathcal{F}(\breve{\varepsilon}_j)$, whenever $\breve{\varepsilon}_i \preceq \breve{\varepsilon}_j, \forall \breve{\varepsilon}_i, \breve{\varepsilon}_j \in \mathcal{P}$, then $(\mathcal{F}, \mathcal{P})$ is called as a contra-lattice ordered interval-valued* *hesitant fuzzy soft set. It can be simply written as* $Contra - \mathcal{L} - \mathcal{IVHFSS}$.

4.2   Main Results

Proposition 4.2.1. *Let* $(\mathcal{F}, \mathcal{P})$ *be a lattice ordered interval-valued hesitant fuzzy soft set over* U. *Then its dual is* $Contra - \mathcal{L} - \mathcal{IVHFSS}$.

Proof. Let $(\mathcal{F}, \mathcal{P})$ be $\mathcal{L} - \mathcal{IVHFSS}$ over U.

Suppose $(\mathcal{F}, \mathcal{Q})$ is its dual.

Then $\mathcal{F}\left(\breve{\delta}_i\right) \subseteq \mathcal{F}\left(\breve{\delta}_j\right) \Leftrightarrow \mathcal{F}\left(\breve{\varepsilon}_i\right) \supseteq \mathcal{F}\left(\breve{\varepsilon}_j\right), \forall \varrho \in U \rightarrow (1)$

Since $\breve{\delta}_i \preceq \breve{\delta}_j \Rightarrow \mathcal{F}\left(\breve{\delta}_i\right) \subseteq \mathcal{F}\left(\breve{\delta}_j\right) \rightarrow (2)$

From $(1), (2)$, we get $\breve{\delta}_i \preceq \breve{\delta}_j \Rightarrow \mathcal{F}\left(\breve{\delta}_i\right) \subseteq \mathcal{F}\left(\breve{\delta}_j\right) \Rightarrow \mathcal{F}\left(\breve{\varepsilon}_i\right) \supseteq \mathcal{F}\left(\breve{\varepsilon}_j\right)$

$\Rightarrow \mathcal{F}\left(\breve{\varepsilon}_i\right) \supseteq \mathcal{F}\left(\breve{\varepsilon}_j\right)$, whenever $\breve{\delta}_i \preceq \breve{\delta}_j$

Hence $(\mathcal{F}, \mathcal{Q})$ is $Contra - \mathcal{L} - \mathcal{IVHFSS}$. $\square$

Proposition 4.2.2. *If* $(\mathcal{G}, \mathcal{P})$ *is* $Contra - \mathcal{L} - \mathcal{IVHFSS}$ *over* U, *then its dual is* $\mathcal{L} - \mathcal{IVHFSS}$.

Proof. Let $(\mathcal{G}, \mathcal{P})$ be $Contra - \mathcal{L} - \mathcal{IVHFSS}$ over U.

Suppose $(\mathcal{G}, \mathcal{Q})$ is its dual.

Then $\mathcal{G}\left(\breve{\delta}_i\right) \subseteq \mathcal{G}\left(\breve{\delta}_j\right) \Leftrightarrow \mathcal{G}\left(\breve{\varepsilon}_i\right) \supseteq \mathcal{G}\left(\breve{\varepsilon}_j\right), \forall \varrho \in \mathrm{U} \to (1)$

Since $\breve{\delta}_i \preceq \breve{\delta}_j \Rightarrow \mathcal{G}\left(\breve{\delta}_i\right) \supseteq \mathcal{G}\left(\breve{\delta}_j\right) \to (2)$

From $(1), (2)$, we get $\breve{\delta}_i \preceq \breve{\delta}_j \Rightarrow \mathcal{G}\left(\breve{\delta}_j\right) \subseteq \mathcal{G}\left(\breve{\delta}_i\right) \Rightarrow \mathcal{G}\left(\breve{\varepsilon}_j\right) \supseteq \mathcal{G}\left(\breve{\varepsilon}_i\right)$

$\therefore \breve{\delta}_i \preceq \breve{\delta}_j \Rightarrow \mathcal{G}\left(\breve{\varepsilon}_i\right) \supseteq \mathcal{G}\left(\breve{\varepsilon}_j\right)$

Hence $(\mathcal{G}, \mathcal{Q})$ is $\mathcal{L} - \mathcal{IVHFSS}$. $\qquad \square$

Example 1.

Consider the $\mathcal{L} - \mathcal{IVHFSS}$ $(\mathcal{F}, \mathcal{P}) = \{\mathcal{F}\left(\breve{\varepsilon}_1\right) = \{< \varrho_1, \{[0.1, 0.2], [0.1, 0.3]\} >,$

$< \varrho_2, \{[0.15, 0.2], [0.2, 0.4]\} >, < \varrho_3, \{[0.3, 0.5], [0.3, 0.5]\} >\},$

$\mathcal{F}\left(\breve{\varepsilon}_2\right) = \{< \varrho_1, \{[0.1, 0.3], [0.15, 0.35]\} >, < \varrho_2, \{[0.23, 0.3], [0.3, 0.4]\} >,$

$< \varrho_3, \{[0.4, 0.55], [0.4, 0.55]\} >\}, \mathcal{F}\left(\breve{\varepsilon}_3\right) = \{< \varrho_1, \{[0.3, 0.5], [0.3, 0.6]\} >,$

$< \varrho_2, \{[0.31, 0.45], [0.4, 0.45]\} >, < \varrho_3, \{[0.45, 0.6], [0.45, 0.6]\} >\}\}.$

The dual of a $(\mathcal{F}, \mathcal{P})$ is $(\mathcal{F}, \mathcal{Q}) = \{\mathcal{F}\left(\breve{\delta}_1\right) = \{< \varrho_1, \{[0.3, 0.5], [0.3, 0.6]\} >,$

$< \varrho_2, \{[0.31, 0.45], [0.4, 0.45]\} >, < \varrho_3, \{[0.45, 0.6], [0.45, 0.6]\} >\},$

$\mathcal{F}\left(\breve{\delta}_2\right) = \{< \varrho_1, \{[0.1, 0.3], [0.15, 0.35]\} >, < \varrho_2, \{[0.23, 0.3], [0.3, 0.4]\} >,$

$< \varrho_3, \{[0.4, 0.55], [0.4, 0.55]\} >\}, \mathcal{F}\left(\breve{\delta}_3\right) = \{< \varrho_1, \{[0.1, 0.2], [0.1, 0.3]\} >,$

$< \varrho_2, \{[0.15, 0.2], [0.2, 0.4]\} >, < \varrho_3, \{[0.3, 0.5], [0.3, 0.5]\} >\}\},$

where $\breve{\delta}_1, \breve{\delta}_2, \breve{\delta}_3$ represents minimum span of time, average span of time and maximum time spent in the game respectively.

Thus we have $\mathcal{F}\left(\breve{\delta}_i\right) \supseteq \mathcal{F}\left(\breve{\delta}_j\right)$ whenever $\breve{\delta}_i \preceq \breve{\delta}_j$.

Hence $(\mathcal{F}, \mathcal{Q})$ is $Contra - \mathcal{L} - \mathcal{IVHFSS}$.

Proposition 4.2.3. *If $(\mathcal{F}, \mathcal{P})$ is an $\mathcal{L} - \mathcal{IVHFSS}$, then there exists an $\mathcal{L}-$isomorphism between $(\mathcal{F}, \mathcal{P})$ and the dual of its dual.*

Proof. Let $(\mathcal{F}, \mathcal{P})$ be an $\mathcal{L} - \mathcal{IVHFSS}$ and $(\mathcal{F}, \mathcal{Q})$ be its dual.

Suppose $(\mathcal{F}, \mathcal{R})$ is the dual of $(\mathcal{F}, \mathcal{Q})$.

Since $(\mathcal{F}, \mathcal{Q})$ is dual of an $\mathcal{L} - \mathcal{IVHFSS}$ $(\mathcal{F}, \mathcal{P})$.

$\Rightarrow (\mathcal{F}, \mathcal{Q})$ is $Contra - \mathcal{L} - \mathcal{IVHFSS}$.

$\Rightarrow (\mathcal{F}, \mathcal{R})$ is $\mathcal{L} - \mathcal{IVHFSS}$.

Now define a map $\phi \colon \mathcal{S}\left(\mathcal{F}_{\mathcal{P}}\right) \to \mathcal{S}\left(\mathcal{F}_{\mathcal{R}}\right)$ by $\phi\left(s\left(h_{F_P}\left(\breve{\varepsilon}_i\right)\right)\right) = \frac{s\left(h_{F_R}(\gamma_i)\right)}{2}$. ϕ is clearly well defined, 1-1 and onto.

Also $\mathcal{F}\left(\breve{\varepsilon}_i\right) \subseteq \mathcal{F}\left(\breve{\varepsilon}_j\right) \Leftrightarrow \mathcal{F}\left(\breve{\delta}_i\right) \supseteq \mathcal{F}\left(\breve{\delta}_j\right), \forall \varrho \in \mathrm{U}$

$\Leftrightarrow \mathcal{F}\left(\breve{\gamma}_i\right) \supseteq \mathcal{F}\left(\breve{\gamma}_j\right), \forall \varrho \in \mathrm{U}$

We have $s\left(h_{F_P}\left(\breve{\varepsilon}_i\right)\right) \subseteq s\left(h_{F_P}\left(\breve{\varepsilon}_j\right)\right) \Leftrightarrow s\left(h_{F_R}\left(\breve{\gamma}_i\right)\right) \subseteq s\left(h_{F_R}\left(\breve{\gamma}_j\right)\right)$

$$\Leftrightarrow \frac{s\left(h_{F_R}(\gamma_i)\right)}{2} \subseteq \frac{s\left(h_{F_R}(\gamma_j)\right)}{2}$$

$$\Leftrightarrow \phi\left(s\left(h_{F_P}\left(\breve{\varepsilon}_i\right)\right)\right) \subseteq \phi\left(s\left(h_{F_P}\left(\breve{\varepsilon}_j\right)\right)\right)$$

Thus $s\left(h_{F_P}\left(\breve{\varepsilon}_i\right)\right) \subseteq s\left(h_{F_P}\left(\breve{\varepsilon}_j\right)\right) \Leftrightarrow \phi\left(s\left(h_{F_P}\left(\breve{\varepsilon}_i\right)\right)\right) \subseteq \phi\left(s\left(h_{F_P}\left(\breve{\varepsilon}_j\right)\right)\right)$

Hence $(\mathcal{F}, \mathcal{P})$ is $\mathcal{L}-$isomorphic to $(\mathcal{F}, \mathcal{R})$. $\qquad\square$

Chapter 5

Application of L-IVHFSS in Decision Making Problems

---

[1] In this chapter, two different algorithms were constructed and the real life problem was solved by using those algorithms via $\mathcal{L} - \mathcal{IVHFSS}$.

5.1 Algorithm for Solving a Real Life Problem

Three players are going to play a series of games each of which has 2 levels in it. Now we construct a $\mathcal{L} - \mathcal{IVHFSS}$ for this problem as follows: The alternatives x_1, x_2 and x_3 represents the three players and the parameters $\breve{\delta}_1, \breve{\delta}_2$ and $\breve{\delta}_3$ denotes the three games repectively as $\breve{\delta}_1$ is the easiest among all, $\breve{\delta}_2$ is little difficult and $\breve{\delta}_3$ is more difficult to play. Thus we compare $\breve{\delta}_1, \breve{\delta}_2, \breve{\delta}_3$ by their difficulties as $\breve{\delta}_1 \preceq \breve{\delta}_2 \preceq \breve{\delta}_3$. A membership function assigns a value $(interval)$ according to the time spent by the players and their

---
[1] Advances in Intelligent Systems and Computing (SPRINGER)

performances separately for 2 levels. If time consumption is less and performance is good, then we assign a minimum interval value, i.e., $[0.1, 0.2]$. Thus we can change the interval value depends on the time consuming and their performance in the respective time period. Thus we have $\mathcal{L} - \mathcal{IVHFSS}$ for this problem as

$$(\mathcal{F}, \mathcal{P}) = \{\mathcal{F}\left(\breve{\delta}_1\right) = \{< x_1, [0.1, 0.2], [0.1, 0.3] >, < x_2, [0.15, 0.2], [0.2, 0.4] >,$$

$$< x_3, [0.3, 0.5], [0.3, 0.5] >\}, \mathcal{F}\left(\breve{\delta}_2\right) = \{< x_1, [0.1, 0.3], [0.15, 0.35] >,$$

$$< x_2, [0.23, 0.3], [0.3, 0.4] >, < x_3, [0.4, 0.55], [0.4, 0.55] >\},$$

$$\mathcal{F}\left(\breve{\delta}_3\right) = \{< x_1, [0.3, 0.5], [0.3, 0.6] >, < x_2, [0.31, 0.45], [0.4, 0.45] >,$$

$$< x_3, [0.45, 0.6], [0.45, 0.6] >\}\}$$

Our aim is to find out which player played all the three games well in short period of time. We use the following algorithm to evaluate the optimal decision making by $\mathcal{L} - \mathcal{IVHFSS}$.

Algorithm

Step 1.

Write a $\mathcal{L} - \mathcal{IVHFSS}$ and find score value for each x_i with respect to each $\breve{\delta}_j$, where $i = 1, 2...n$ and $j = 1, 2...m$

$(\mathcal{F}, \mathcal{P}) = \{\mathcal{F}\left(\breve{\delta}_1\right) = \{< x_1, [0.1, 0.2], [0.1, 0.3] >, < x_2, [0.15, 0.2], [0.2, 0.4] >,$

$< x_3, [0.3, 0.5], [0.3, 0.5] >\},$

$\mathcal{F}\left(\breve{\delta}_2\right) = \{< x_1, [0.1, 0.3], [0.15, 0.35] >,$

$< x_2, [0.23, 0.3], [0.3, 0.4] >, < x_3, [0.4, 0.55], [0.4, 0.55] >\},$

$\mathcal{F}\left(\breve{\delta}_3\right) = \{< x_1, [0.3, 0.5], [0.3, 0.6] >, < x_2, [0.31, 0.45], [0.4, 0.45] >,$

$< x_3, [0.45, 0.6], [0.45, 0.6] >\}\}$

$s\left(h_1\left(x_1\right)\right) = \frac{1}{2}[0.2, 0.5] = [0.1, 0.25]$

$s\left(h_1\left(x_2\right)\right) = \frac{1}{2}[0.35, 0.6] = [0.175, 0.3]$

$s\left(h_1\left(x_3\right)\right) = \frac{1}{2}[0.6, 1] = [0.3, 0.5]$

$s\left(h_2\left(x_1\right)\right) = \frac{1}{2}[0.25, 0.65] = [0.125, 0.325]$

$s\left(h_2\left(x_2\right)\right) = \frac{1}{2}[0.53, 0.7] = [0.265, 0.35]$

$s\left(h_2\left(x_3\right)\right) = \frac{1}{2}[0.8, 1.1] = [0.4, 0.55]$

$s\left(h_3\left(x_1\right)\right) = \frac{1}{2}[0.6, 1.1] = [0.3, 0.55]$

$s\left(h_3\left(x_2\right)\right) = \frac{1}{2}[0.71, 0.9] = [0.355, 0.45]$

$s\left(h_3\left(x_3\right)\right) = \frac{1}{2}[0.9, 1.2] = [0.45, 0.6]$

Step 2.

Find the mid value for each score function value and write it as m_{ij}.

$$m_{ij} = \begin{bmatrix} 0.175 & 0.225 & 0.425 \\ 0.2375 & 0.3075 & 0.4025 \\ 0.4 & 0.475 & 0.525 \end{bmatrix}$$

Step 3.

Assign weight w_{ij} for each x_i with respect to each $\breve{\delta}_j$ by $+1$ if corresponding midvalue

< 0.5 *and* 0 *if* ≥ 0.5.

$$w_{ij} = \begin{bmatrix} 1 & 1 & 1 \\ 1 & 1 & 1 \\ 1 & 1 & 0 \end{bmatrix}$$

Step 4.

Compute $P_i = \sum_{j=1}^{n} (m_{ij}.w_{ij})$

$P_1 = (0.175)(1) + (0.225)(1) + (0.425)(1) = 0.825$

$P_2 = (0.2375)(1) + (0.3075)(1) + (0.4025)(1) = 0.9475$

$P_3 = (0.4)(1) + (0.475)(1) + (0.525)(0) = 0.875$

Step 5.

Choose the maximum of P_is as the optimal value.

$P_2 = 0.9475$ is the maximum value among all P_is.

Thus we have to select the optimal decision making as the second player x_2 who performed well in all three games in a short peroid of time.

5.2 Application of L-IVHFSS in Decision Making Problem

In this section, the new improved algorithm was designed and the problem of decision

making on $\mathcal{L} - \mathcal{IVHFSS}$ was solved by this interesting algorithm.

Definition 5.2.1. *Let $(\mathcal{F}, \mathcal{P})$ be an $\mathcal{L} - \mathcal{IVHFSS}$ over U. Then $\mathcal{L}$-optimistic interval-*

valued fuzzy soft set $(\mathcal{F}_{\mathcal{L}+}, \mathcal{P})$ is defined as

$$
\begin{aligned}
(\mathcal{F}_{\mathcal{L}+}, \mathcal{P}) &= \{< x, \mathcal{F}_{\mathcal{L}+}\left(\breve{\delta}\right)(x) > |x \in U\} \\
&= \{< x, \vee \gamma_{\mathcal{L}}^{\sigma(k)} > |x \in U\},
\end{aligned}
$$

$\forall \breve{\delta} \in \mathcal{P}$ and $\forall k = 1, 2..n,$

where $\gamma_{\mathcal{L}}^{\sigma(k)} = [\gamma_{\mathcal{L}}^{\sigma(k)(L)}, \gamma_{\mathcal{L}}^{\sigma(k)(U)}] \in \mathcal{F}\left(\breve{\delta}\right)(x)$

Definition 5.2.2. *Let $(\mathcal{F}, \mathcal{P})$ be an $\mathcal{L} - \mathcal{IVHFSS}$ over U. Then $\mathcal{L}$-neutral interval-*

valued fuzzy soft set $(\mathcal{F}_{\mathcal{L}\sim}, \mathcal{P})$ is defined as

$$
\begin{aligned}
(\mathcal{F}_{\mathcal{L}\sim}, \mathcal{P}) &= \{< x, \mathcal{F}_{\mathcal{L}\sim}\left(\breve{\delta}\right)(x) > |x \in U\} \\
&= \{< x, \sum_{k=1}^{n} \frac{\gamma_{\mathcal{L}}^{\sigma(k)}}{n} > |x \in U\},
\end{aligned}
$$

$\forall \breve{\delta} \in \mathcal{P}$ and $\forall k = 1, 2..n$, where $\gamma_{\mathcal{L}}^{\sigma(k)} = [\gamma_{\mathcal{L}}^{\sigma(k)(L)}, \gamma_{\mathcal{L}}^{\sigma(k)(U)}] \in \mathcal{F}\left(\breve{\delta}\right)(x)$

Definition 5.2.3. *Let* $(\mathcal{F}, \mathcal{P})$ *be an* $\mathcal{L} - \mathcal{IVHFSS}$ *over* U. *Then* $\mathcal{L}$-*pessimistic interval-valued fuzzy soft set* $(\mathcal{F}_{\mathcal{L}-}, \mathcal{P})$ *is defined as*

$$(\mathcal{F}_{\mathcal{L}-}, \mathcal{P}) = \{< x, \mathcal{F}_{\mathcal{L}-}\left(\breve{\delta}\right)(x) > |x \in U\}$$

$$= \{< x, \wedge\gamma_{\mathcal{L}}^{\sigma(k)} > |x \in U\},$$

$\forall \breve{\delta} \in \mathcal{P}$ and $\forall k = 1, 2..n$, where $\gamma_{\mathcal{L}}^{\sigma(k)} = [\gamma_{\mathcal{L}}^{\sigma(k)(L)}, \gamma_{\mathcal{L}}^{\sigma(k)(U)}] \in \mathcal{F}\left(\breve{\delta}\right)(x)$

Definition 5.2.4. *Let* $(\mathcal{F}, \mathcal{P})$ *be an* $\mathcal{L} - \mathcal{IVHFSS}$ *over* U *and* $(I, \mathcal{P})$ *be an IVFS. Then*

$$\alpha^{\sigma(k)} = \begin{cases} 1 & if \gamma^{\sigma(k)} \geq I\left(\breve{\delta}\right) \\ 0 & if \gamma^{\sigma(k)} < I\left(\breve{\delta}\right) \end{cases},$$

$\forall \breve{\delta} \in \mathcal{P}, \forall \gamma^{\sigma(k)} \in \mathcal{F}\left(\breve{\delta}\right)$ *and* $\forall k = 1, 2..n$.

Then $(I, \mathcal{P})$ *is called an* $\mathcal{L}$-*threshold interval-valued fuzzy set. Also an* $\mathcal{L}$-*level hesitant fuzzy soft set* $(\mathcal{F}_{\mathcal{L}I}, \mathcal{P})$ *with respect to* $(I, \mathcal{P})$ *is defined as*

$$(\mathcal{F}_{\mathcal{L}I}, \mathcal{P}) = \{< x, \mathcal{F}_{\mathcal{L}I}\left(\breve{\delta}\right)(x) > |x \in U\}$$

$$= \{< x, \{\alpha^{\sigma(k)}\} > |x \in U\},$$

$\forall \breve{\delta} \in \mathcal{P}, \forall k = 1, 2...n$

Definition 5.2.5. *Let* $(\mathcal{F}, \mathcal{P})$ *be an* $\mathcal{L} - \mathcal{IVHFSS}$ *over* U *and* $(J, \mathcal{P})$ *be an IVFS.*

Then $\beta^{\sigma(k)} = \begin{cases} 1 & if\ \gamma^{\sigma(k)} \leq J\left(\breve{\delta}\right) \\ 0 & if\ \gamma^{\sigma(k)} > J\left(\breve{\delta}\right) \end{cases}$,

$\forall \breve{\delta} \in \mathcal{P}, \forall \gamma^{\sigma(k)} \in \mathcal{F}\left(\breve{\delta}\right)$ *and* $\forall k = 1, 2..n.$

Then $(J, \mathcal{P})$ *is called a contra-*$\mathcal{L}$*-threshold interval-valued fuzzy set. Also a contra-*$\mathcal{L}$-

level hesitant fuzzy soft set $(\mathcal{F}_{\mathcal{L}J}, \mathcal{P})$ *with respect to* $(J, \mathcal{P})$ *is defined as*

$$(\mathcal{F}_{\mathcal{L}J}, \mathcal{P}) = \{< x, \mathcal{F}_{\mathcal{L}J}\left(\breve{\delta}\right)(x) > | x \in U\}$$

$$= \{< x, \{\beta^{\sigma(k)}\} > | x \in U\},$$

$\forall \breve{\delta} \in \mathcal{P}, \forall k = 1, 2...n$

Definition 5.2.6. *Let* U *be an universal set and* $\mathcal{P}$ *be a parameter set. Let* $(\mathcal{F}, \mathcal{P})$ *be*

$\mathcal{L} - \mathcal{IVHFSS}$. *Then*

(i) $\ddot{\vee}_{x \in U}\{\mathcal{F}\left(\breve{\delta}\right)(x)\} = \mathcal{F}\left(\breve{\delta}\right)(x_k)\ if\ \mathcal{F}\left(\breve{\delta}\right)(x_i) \subseteq \mathcal{F}\left(\breve{\delta}\right)(x_j) \subseteq \mathcal{F}\left(\breve{\delta}\right)(x_k)$

(ii) $\ddot{\wedge}_{x \in U}\{\mathcal{F}\left(\breve{\delta}\right)(x)\} = \mathcal{F}\left(\breve{\delta}\right)(x_i)\ if\ \mathcal{F}\left(\breve{\delta}\right)(x_i) \subseteq \mathcal{F}\left(\breve{\delta}\right)(x_j) \subseteq \mathcal{F}\left(\breve{\delta}\right)(x_k)$

(iii) $\ddot{\vee}\ddot{\wedge}_{x \in U}\{\mathcal{F}\left(\breve{\delta}\right)(x)\} = \mathcal{F}\left(\breve{\delta}\right)(x_j)\ if\ \mathcal{F}\left(\breve{\delta}\right)(x_i) \subseteq \mathcal{F}\left(\breve{\delta}\right)(x_j) \subseteq \mathcal{F}\left(\breve{\delta}\right)(x_k).$

Definition 5.2.7. *Let* $(\mathcal{F}, \mathcal{P})$ *be an* $\mathcal{L} - \mathcal{IVHFSS}$ *over* U *and* $(\mathcal{F}_{\mathcal{L}+}, \mathcal{P})$ *be an* $\mathcal{L}$-

optimistic IVFSS over U. *Then* $Max_{\mathcal{L}}$*-threshold of*

$\mathcal{L} - \mathcal{IVHFSS}$ is defined as $\mathcal{F}_{Max-\mathcal{L}}\left(\breve{\delta}\right) = \ddot{\vee}\mathcal{F}_{\mathcal{L}+}\left(\breve{\delta}\right)(x), \forall \breve{\delta} \in \mathcal{P}$, where $x \in$ U. The $\mathcal{L}$-top level Hfss of $(\mathcal{F}, \mathcal{P})$ with respect to $Max_{\mathcal{L}}$-threshold is defined as $(\mathcal{F}_{Max-\mathcal{L}}, \mathcal{P}) = \{< x, \mathcal{F}_{Max-\mathcal{L}}\left(\breve{\delta}\right)(x) > | x \in U\}.$

Definition 5.2.8. Let $(\mathcal{F}, \mathcal{P})$ be an $\mathcal{L} - \mathcal{IVHFSS}$ over U and $(\mathcal{F}_{\mathcal{L}\sim}, \mathcal{P})$ be an $\mathcal{L}$-neutral IVFSS over U. Then $Mid_{\mathcal{L}}$-threshold of $\mathcal{L} - \mathcal{IVHFSS}$ is defined as $\mathcal{F}_{Mid-\mathcal{L}}\left(\breve{\delta}\right) = \ddot{\vee}\ddot{\wedge}\mathcal{F}_{\mathcal{L}\sim}\left(\breve{\delta}\right)(x), \forall \breve{\delta} \in \mathcal{P}$, where $x \in$ U. The $\mathcal{L}$-mid level Hfss of $(\mathcal{F}, \mathcal{P})$ with respect to $Mid_{\mathcal{L}}$-threshold is defined as $(\mathcal{F}_{Mid-\mathcal{L}}, \mathcal{P}) = \{< x, \mathcal{F}_{Mid-\mathcal{L}}\left(\breve{\delta}\right)(x) > | x \in U\}.$

Definition 5.2.9. Let $(\mathcal{F}, \mathcal{P})$ be an $\mathcal{L} - \mathcal{IVHFSS}$ over U and $(\mathcal{F}_{\mathcal{L}-}, \mathcal{P})$ be an $\mathcal{L}$-pessimistic IVFSS over U. Then $Min_{\mathcal{L}}$-threshold of $\mathcal{L} - \mathcal{IVHFSS}$ is defined as $\mathcal{F}_{Min-\mathcal{L}}\left(\breve{\delta}\right) = \ddot{\wedge}\mathcal{F}_{\mathcal{L}-}\left(\breve{\delta}\right)(x), \forall \breve{\delta} \in \mathcal{P}$, where $x \in U$. The $\mathcal{L}$-low level Hfss of $(\mathcal{F}, \mathcal{P})$ with respect to $Min_{\mathcal{L}}$-threshold is defined as $(\mathcal{F}_{Min-\mathcal{L}}, \mathcal{P}) = \{< x, \mathcal{F}_{Min-\mathcal{L}}\left(\breve{\delta}\right)(x) > | x \in U\}.$

An improved algorithm for solving a real life problem via L-IVHFSS

Consider x_1, x_2 and x_3 represent three sets of diet and $\breve{\delta}_1, \breve{\delta}_2, \breve{\delta}_3, \breve{\delta}_4$ and $\breve{\delta}_5$ represent protein, carbohydrates, fat, water and vitamins respectively. Thus the given $\mathcal{L} - \mathcal{IVHFSS}$

$(\mathcal{F}, \mathcal{P})$ represents the amount of protein, carbohydrates, fat, water and vitamins present in the three sets of diets and this data is collected from 2 nutrionists. Now the problem is that the decision maker has to select the best diet set among the three given sets of diets. For this situation, We will choose the most correct decision by constructing an algorithm as follows:

Step:1

Write a given $\mathcal{L} - \mathcal{IVHFSS}\,(\mathcal{F}, \mathcal{P})$

Given $(\mathcal{F}, \mathcal{P}) = \{\mathcal{F}\left(\breve{\delta}_1\right) = \{< x_1, \{[0.4, 0.6], [0.4, 0.65]\} >,$

$< x_2, \{[0.2, 0.31], [0.3, 0.5]\} >, < x_3, \{[0.45, 0.5], [0.4, 0.6]\} >\},$

$\mathcal{F}\left(\breve{\delta}_2\right) = \{< x_1, \{[0.5, 0.7], [0.4, 0.5]\} >, < x_2, \{[0.35, 0.55], [0.2, 0.3]\} >,$

$< x_3, \{[0.4, 0.5], [0.55, 0.65]\} >\}, \mathcal{F}\left(\breve{\delta}_3\right) = \{< x_1, \{[0.44, 0.6], [0.51, 0.63]\} >,$

$< x_2, \{[0.25, 0.5], [0.33, 0.4]\} >, < x_3, \{[0.47, 0.6], [0.5, 0.6]\} >\},$

$\mathcal{F}\left(\breve{\delta}_4\right) = \{< x_1, \{[0.4, 0.55], [0.58, 0.7]\} >, < x_2, \{[0.3, 0.5], [0.35, 0.45]\} >,$

$< x_3, \{[0.5, 0.6], [0.5, 0.7]\} >\}, \mathcal{F}\left(\breve{\delta}_5\right) = \{< x_1, \{[0.51, 0.6], [0.5, 0.67]\} >,$

$< x_2, \{[0.2, 0.4], [0.5, 0.6]\} >, < x_3, \{[0.5, 0.65], [0.55, 0.7]\} >\}\}$

Step:2

(i) *Find $Max_{\mathcal{L}}$-threshold of $(\mathcal{F}, \mathcal{P})$.*

$$\mathcal{F}_{Max-\mathcal{L}}\left(\breve{\delta}\right) = \{< \breve{\delta}_1, [0.4, 0.65] >, < \breve{\delta}_2, [0.5, 0.7] >, < \breve{\delta}_3, [0.51, 0.63] >,$$

$$< \breve{\delta}_4, [0.58, 0.7] >, < \breve{\delta}_5, [0.55, 0.7] >\}$$

(ii) *Find $\mathcal{L}$-top level hesitant fuzzy soft set $(\mathcal{F}_{Max-\mathcal{L}}, \mathcal{P})$ of $(\mathcal{F}, \mathcal{P})$.*

$$(\mathcal{F}_{Max-\mathcal{L}}, \mathcal{P}) = \{\mathcal{F}\left(\breve{\delta}_1\right) = \{< x_1, \{0, 1\} >, < x_2, \{0, 0\} >, < x_3, \{0, 0\} >\},$$

$$\mathcal{F}\left(\breve{\delta}_2\right) = \{< x_1, \{1, 0\} >, < x_2, \{0, 0\} >, < x_3, \{0, 0\} >\},$$

$$\mathcal{F}\left(\breve{\delta}_3\right) = \{< x_1, \{0, 1\} >, < x_2, \{0, 0\} >, < x_3, \{0, 0\} >\},$$

$$\mathcal{F}\left(\breve{\delta}_4\right) = \{< x_1, \{0, 1\} >, < x_2, \{0, 0\} >, < x_3, \{0, 0\} >\},$$

$$\mathcal{F}\left(\breve{\delta}_5\right) = \{< x_1, \{0, 0\} >, < x_2, \{0, 0\} >, < x_3, \{0, 1\} >\}\}$$

(iii) *Assign weight w_{j+} for each parameter $\breve{\delta}_j$, where $j = 1, 2, , , m$ for $(\mathcal{F}_{Max-\mathcal{L}}, \mathcal{P})$.*

$$w_{1+} = 0.5, w_{2+} = 0.45, w_{3+} = 0.2, w_{4+} = 0.4, w_{5+} = 0.5$$

(iv) *Draw a table for* $(\mathcal{F}_{Max-\mathcal{L}}, \mathcal{P}, w_{j+})$.

U	$(\mathcal{P}, w_{i+})$					p_i
	$\breve{\delta}_1, w_{1+} = 0.5$	$\breve{\delta}_2, w_{2+} = 0.45$	$\breve{\delta}_3, w_{3+} = 0.2$	$\breve{\delta}_4, w_{4+} = 0.4$	$\breve{\delta}_5, w_{5+} = 0.5$	
x_1	$\{0,1\}$	$\{1,0\}$	$\{0,1\}$	$\{0,1\}$	$\{0,0\}$	1.55
x_2	$\{0,0\}$	$\{0,0\}$	$\{0,0\}$	$\{0,0\}$	$\{0,0\}$	0
x_3	$\{0,0\}$	$\{0,0\}$	$\{0,0\}$	$\{0,0\}$	$\{0,1\}$	0.5

Step:3

(i) *Find* $Mid_{\mathcal{L}}$*-threshold of* $(\mathcal{F}, \mathcal{P})$.

$$\mathcal{F}_{Mid-\mathcal{L}}\left(\breve{\delta}\right) = \{< \breve{\delta}_1, [0.4, 0.625] >, < \breve{\delta}_2, [0.475, 0.575] >,$$
$$< \breve{\delta}_3, [0.485, 0.6] >, < \breve{\delta}_4, [0.49, 0.625] >, < \breve{\delta}_5, [0.505, 0.635] >\}$$

(ii) *Find* $\mathcal{L}$*-mid level hesitant fuzzy soft set* $(\mathcal{F}_{Max-\mathcal{L}}, \mathcal{P})$ *of* $(\mathcal{F}, \mathcal{P})$.

$$(\mathcal{F}_{Mid-\mathcal{L}}, \mathcal{P}) = \{\mathcal{F}\left(\breve{\delta}_1\right) = \{< x_1, \{0,1\} >, < x_2, \{0,0\} >, < x_3, \{0,0\} >\},$$
$$\mathcal{F}\left(\breve{\delta}_2\right) = \{< x_1, \{1,0\} >, < x_2, \{0,0\} >, < x_3, \{0,1\} >\},$$
$$\mathcal{F}\left(\breve{\delta}_3\right) = \{< x_1, \{0,1\} >, < x_2, \{0,0\} >, < x_3, \{0,1\} >\},$$
$$\mathcal{F}\left(\breve{\delta}_4\right) = \{< x_1, \{0,1\} >, < x_2, \{0,0\} >, < x_3, \{0,0\} >\},$$
$$\mathcal{F}\left(\breve{\delta}_5\right) = \{< x_1, \{0,1\} >, < x_2, \{0,0\} >, < x_3, \{1,1\} >\}\}$$

(iii) *Calculate weight* $w_{j\sim} = \frac{w_{j\pm}}{2}$ *for each parameter* $\breve{\delta}_j$, *where* $j = 1, 2, , , m$ *for* $(\mathcal{F}_{Mid-\mathcal{L}}, \mathcal{P})$.
$w_{1\sim} = 0.25, w_{2\sim} = 0.225, w_{3\sim} = 0.1, w_{4\sim} = 0.2, w_{5\sim} = 0.25$

(iv) *Draw a table for* $(\mathcal{F}_{Mid-\mathcal{L}}, \mathcal{P}, w_{j\sim})$.

U	$(\mathcal{P}, w_{i\sim})$					q_i
	$\breve{\delta}_1, w_{1\sim} = 0.25$	$\breve{\delta}_2, w_{2\sim} = 0.225$	$\breve{\delta}_3, w_{3\sim} = 0.1$	$\breve{\delta}_4, w_{4\sim} = 0.2$	$\breve{\delta}_5, w_{5\sim} = 0.25$	
x_1	$\{0,1\}$	$\{1,0\}$	$\{0,1\}$	$\{0,1\}$	$\{0,1\}$	1.025
x_2	$\{0,0\}$	$\{0,0\}$	$\{0,0\}$	$\{0,0\}$	$\{0,0\}$	0
x_3	$\{0,0\}$	$\{0,1\}$	$\{0,1\}$	$\{0,0\}$	$\{1,1\}$	0.825

Step:4

(i) *Find* $Min_{\mathcal{L}}$*-threshold of* $(\mathcal{F}, \mathcal{P})$.
$$\mathcal{F}_{Min-\mathcal{L}}\left(\breve{\delta}\right) = \{< \breve{\delta}_1, [0.2, 0.31] >, < \breve{\delta}_2, [0.2, 0.3] >, < \breve{\delta}_3, [0.25, 0.4] >,$$
$$< \breve{\delta}_4, [0.3, 0.45] >, < \breve{\delta}_5, [0.2, 0.4] >\}$$

(ii) *Find* $\mathcal{L}$*-low level hesitant fuzzy soft set* $(\mathcal{F}_{Min-\mathcal{L}}, \mathcal{P})$ *of* $(\mathcal{F}, \mathcal{P})$.
$$(\mathcal{F}_{Min-\mathcal{L}}, \mathcal{P}) = \{\mathcal{F}\left(\breve{\delta}_1\right) = \{< x_1, \{0, 0\} >, < x_2, \{1, 0\} >, < x_3, \{0, 0\} >\},$$
$$\mathcal{F}\left(\breve{\delta}_2\right) = \{< x_1, \{0, 0\} >, < x_2, \{0, 1\} >, < x_3, \{0, 0\} >\},$$
$$\mathcal{F}\left(\breve{\delta}_3\right) = \{< x_1, \{0, 0\} >, < x_2, \{0, 0\} >, < x_3, \{0, 0\} >\},$$
$$\mathcal{F}\left(\breve{\delta}_4\right) = \{< x_1, \{0, 0\} >, < x_2, \{0, 1\} >, < x_3, \{0, 0\} >\},$$
$$\mathcal{F}\left(\breve{\delta}_5\right) = \{< x_1, \{0, 0\} >, < x_2, \{1, 0\} >, < x_3, \{0, 0\} >\}\}$$

(iii) *Calculate* $w_{j-} = 1 - w_{j+}$ *for each parameter* $\breve{\delta}_j$, *where* $j = 1, 2, , , m$ *for* $(\mathcal{F}_{Min-\mathcal{L}}, \mathcal{P})$.
$w_{1-} = 0.5, w_{2-} = 0.55, w_{3-} = 0.8, w_{4-} = 0.6, w_{5-} = 0.5$

(iv) *Draw a table for* $(\mathcal{F}_{Min-\mathcal{L}}, \mathcal{P}, w_{j-})$.

U	$(\mathcal{P}, w_{i-})$					r_i
	$\breve{\delta}_1, w_{1-} = 0.5$	$\breve{\delta}_2, w_{2-} = 0.55$	$\breve{\delta}_3, w_{3-} = 0.8$	$\breve{\delta}_4, w_{4-} = 0.6$	$\breve{\delta}_5, w_{5-} = 0.5$	
x_1	$\{0, 0\}$	$\{0, 0\}$	$\{0, 0\}$	$\{0, 0\}$	$\{0, 0\}$	0
x_2	$\{1, 0\}$	$\{0, 1\}$	$\{0, 0\}$	$\{0, 1\}$	$\{1, 0\}$	2.15
x_3	$\{0, 0\}$	$\{0, 0\}$	$\{0, 0\}$	$\{0, 0\}$	$\{0, 0\}$	0

Step:5

(i) *Calculate* $p_i = \sum_{j=1}^{m} \mathcal{F}_{Max-\mathcal{L}}\left(\breve{\delta}\right)(x_i) w_{j+}$
$p_1 = 1.55, p_2 = 0, p_3 = 0.5$

(ii) *Calculate* $q_i = \sum_{j=1}^{m} \mathcal{F}_{Mid-\mathcal{L}}\left(\breve{\delta}\right)(x_i) w_{j\sim}$
$q_1 = 1.025, q_2 = 0, q_3 = 0.825$

(iii) *Calculate* $r_i = \sum_{j=1}^{m} \mathcal{F}_{Min-\mathcal{L}}\left(\breve{\delta}\right)(x_i) w_{j-}$
$r_1 = 0, r_2 = 2.15, r_3 = 0$

Step:6

Calculate $C_i = \frac{p_i + q_i}{2} - r_i$, for each $i = 1, 2, ...n$
$C_1 = 1.2875, C_2 = -2.15, C_3 = 0.6625$
Choose the optimal alternative as x_i whose C_i value is maximum.
Hence the optimal alternative is x_1.

Decision:

Thus the decision maker choose the optimal alternative x_1, as the best diet. In the first algo-rithm, we analysed the decision making problem in a neutral view and solved the problem using aggregation method. But here we examined the problem in different views such as optimistic, pessimistic and neutral. Thus we inspected the problem in many dimensions to get the precise decision.

Milton Keynes UK
Ingram Content Group UK Ltd.
UKHW020931231123
433129UK00016B/837